GROWING PAINS

GROWING PAINS

What to do when your children turn into teenagers

Dr David Bennett

Illustrations by Jack Newnham

THORSONS PUBLISHING GROUP

First UK Edition published 1987

First published in Australia by
Doubleday Australia Pty Limited
91 Mars Road, Lane Cove, NSW 2066 in 1987

British Library Cataloguing in Publication Data

Bennett, David
Growing Pains: What to do when your children turn into teenagers
1. Adolescence
I. Title
305.2'35

ISBN 0-7225-1643-6

Published by Thorsons Publishers Limited,
Wellingborough, Northamptonshire, NN8 2RQ, England

Printed in Great Britain by Hazell, Watson and Viney
Limited, Aylesbury, Buckinghamshire

Contents

Dedication

To my wife Anne, and my children: Lisa, Adam, Sari and Nathan, whose love, support and patience enabled me to complete this book.

Acknowledgements

This book nearly wasn't written. When Harry Bauer lent me a word processor, things took a distinct turn for the better, for which I (and my publishers) are immensely grateful.

Of course, *Growing Pains* did not arise out of a vacuum. My training and subsequent career in adolescent medicine are certainly relevant. I owe a particular debt of gratitude to three men and would like to acknowledge them here: Dr Murray Williams, for helping to point me in that direction and for his ongoing support and encouragement; Dr William A. Daniel Jr, for generously and thoroughly showing me how it's done (in Alabama); and Dr John Yu, for giving me the opportunity to do it here in Australia, at an important, trend setting Children's Hospital.

In drafting the book, I drew also on the expertise of the following admired colleagues, to whom I wish to express my sincere thanks: Dr Michael Schwarz (adolescent and family psychiatrist); Ms Helen Tolstoshev (adolescent health worker); Dr Kate Steinbeck (endocrinologist); Dr Susan Fleming (gynaecologist); Dr Virginia Furner (general practitioner); Dr Susan Towns (paediatrician/adolescent physician); Ms Sally Denshire (occupational therapist); Ms Christine Singleton (social worker/family therapist); Mr Kevin Donnelly (educator/personal development expert); Ms Louise Rowling (health and drug educator); and other colleagues at the Adolescent Medical Unit who provided ideas and moral support.

Needless to say, my wife and children are well deserving of the dedication of this book to them. Their support, understanding and (at times) bemused interest, helped keep me on an even keel. I also wish to warmly thank the numerous parents who offered advice and encouragement (including some friendly, middle aged strangers to whom I introduced myself on trains and buses); the following people kindly assisted by reading and commenting on the final draft: Peter McKay, Audrey Christie, Jan Hyde, Lesley McKay, John and Myrna Deverell, Ian and Glenys McLaine. And a particular thank you to Kathy Albury, a young person who was willing to provide a current and authentic youth perspective where this seemed warranted.

Finally, and most importantly, I record my heartfelt thanks to my wonderful editor, Kirsty Melville. Her good humour, wisdom, confidence and unstinting support, kept the whole process ticking along. *Growing Pains* is assuredly as much her work as mine.

Foreword

Growing up is often hard and much of this is due to our difficulty and embarrassment in talking about issues with our family, which we can freely joke and laugh about with our friends—subjects like sex. Sometimes the difficulty is caused by not knowing where to seek information, or when the seeking of information is, in itself, embarrassing. At other times family or friends don't have the answers.

More people are turning to books like *Growing Pains* to provide the facts and to help us understand why we and others around us feel the way we do.

David Bennett is a special father with his own teenagers, but who, in professional life, devotes his time to talking to young people and helping them. The result is this book, factual but not didactic, with a style tinged with the humour of life. It is a storehouse of common sense which draws the broad limits of normality and which will help adolescents and their families understand what is happening to them. It is a welcome addition to the books written for the ordinary family by an expert.

J. S. YU
General Superintendent
The Children's Hospital
Camperdown, New South Wales,
Australia

Introduction

Most teenagers are perfectly normal. They spend their time doing the normal things that teenagers do: dominating the telephone; playing music unbearably loud; never tidying their bedroom; staying out late; and being incredibly moody. They simply don't understand why parents get upset. 'Don't they know what's normal?'

Well, that's the point—perhaps they don't! Is it normal, for example, for a fourteen year old girl to spend hours alone writing mysteriously in a diary, or just staring dreamily into space? Is it normal for a fifteen year old boy to have such big feet or to be so noisy and clumsy? Why do kids eat, talk and wash so much (or so little)?

Research shows that parents are generally not well prepared for their children's adolescence, especially the first time; and even experienced parents can be taken by surprise. For both parents and kids, in fact, there is frequently a vague and uncomfortable feeling that things are not completely under control, mostly because they're not! It is an unsettling time because so much change is happening—in both the lives of teenagers and their parents. Clearly, there is a great deal to understand and cope with together.

Most people would probably agree that being a parent is easier with younger children. Despite sleepless nights in early childhood or the demands of the toddler and primary school child, somehow it was easier then—or so it seems when those teenage years strike.

Of course, it is during these childhood years that many patterns of behaviour and interaction are set. The building blocks are assembled and the child enters adolescence with many of his or her ideas about the world clearly in place. Yet during the next few, short years, a staggering amount of growth and development will occur. That once familiar angelic child will become unrecognisable—well, at least for a time. And throughout it all, parents remain, by and large, the most important people in their children's lives.

What teenagers do not always recognise or readily understand, however, is that parents too are often experiencing confusion and conflict in their own lives. These are frequently related to the transitional upheavals of middle age, although difficulties can arise within families for other reasons as well. The ways in which adolescence and 'middlescence' coincide, and the impact of the two generations upon each other, are issues that I will discuss in some detail.

I have written *Growing Pains* primarily for parents, although other people involved in the general or health care of young people will also find it useful. The basic idea is this: if we can all gain a keener appreciation of what's going on (with our kids and ourselves), what to worry about and when to roll with the punches, we'll know how to handle ourselves in the trickier situations, and everybody will be just that little bit better off.

GROWING UP

Am I NORMAL?
Am I NORMAL?
Am I NORMAL?
Am I NORMAL?
Am I NORMAL?
Am I NORMAL?

CHAPTER ONE

The Perils of Puberty

Puberty can be an exciting time for young people, but clearly there are troubling moments for everyone involved. Adolescents are normally preoccupied with their changing bodies, but their anxieties and self-concerns are often unstated and hence poorly understood, even by those who care about them the most.

Perhaps one reason for this is that a parent's personal recollections of those often embarrassing experiences and noteworthy events have been mercifully dulled by time (possibly some sort of protective device instituted by Nature). Would we actually want to remember it, in all its agonising detail, even if we could? No wonder our children's puberty often takes us by surprise, particularly with our first born. For one thing, it forces us to acknowledge the passage of time—a quick decade, more or less—and to recall and relive the experience ourselves, which is also the case with many other aspects of our children's adolescence.

In the midst of all their hormonal and bodily turmoil, however, the all-encompassing question that adolescents are asking is, 'Am I normal?' Someone must answer. Parents can help enormously by having some idea about what is normal, by knowing what to expect, by tolerating embarrassment and distress, (even when it seems unwarranted), and by providing perspective and reassurance.

Is This Really Me?

The normal changes that are taking place during puberty are confusing, at the very least. At the very worst, kids may wonder if their body really belongs to them—it certainly may not feel like it! They are undergoing the most impressive and rapid alterations in size and shape that they will ever experience, not to mention adding totally new bits and pieces! In developing sexually, they are also moving inexorably towards reproductive maturity which adds a very special dimension to their lives, and even to yours.

How Does It Start?

No one knows precisely what triggers the sequence of events that starts puberty off. The initial message comes from the brain, and then most of the responsibility for what follows rests with the pituitary—the 'master gland' that conducts an orchestra of hormones. Once underway, there's no turning back.

As a general rule, the earliest visible changes of puberty are evident around the age of 10 or 11 for girls (usually by the appearance of breast buds) and 11 or 12 for boys (usually by a slight darkening and roughening of the skin of the scrotum). For everyone, however, the time for getting started is a uniquely individual matter and is influenced by such factors as heredity, nutrition and general health.

Total Transformation

Prior to puberty, any differences in the shapes of children's bodies of both sexes are hardly noticeable. The sex hormones, oestrogen and testosterone, soon change that. As girls broaden in the hips, boys broaden in the shoulders and everybody's supposed to like the shape they've become, which of course seldom happens.

Boys experience a major increase in the amount of muscle. The chest thickens, biceps flex, and we have a manly hunk in the making. Even thin guys, who are often very conscious of their stature, double their muscle mass during puberty (under the influence of muscle-making testosterone), whereas it only increases by about half in girls. There are few boys who would not wish this process to occur earlier or more satisfactorily. Some do their very best to help it along.

In girls, important things are happening to their fat stores (adipose tissue):

- There's an increase in the total amount of fat (often referred to as 'puppy fat' although it actually stays around); and eventually, fat constitutes around 25 per cent of girls' body weight (compared to a mere 15 per cent or so of boys)
- There's an obvious increase in fat on hips, thighs and breasts, producing the female shape that women naturally have

These days, with thinness being all the rage, a good thing for parents to tell their daughters is how normal, appropriate and attractive these changes are. Somehow, we have to amend the notion that Nature has got it all wrong.

What Happens to Girls?

No one should be in any doubt that kids are sensitive about puberty. When my daughter heard that I had been invited to speak on this subject to her sixth class, she earnestly suggested, 'Please don't go over the top Dad. We're only children, you know!'

Some girls don't think twice about the development of their breasts, but others take the whole issue very seriously. They are, after all, inevitably in the public eye. While vulgar barbs from fascinated pubescent boys (often a brother) are a common enough hazard, even a supposedly complimentary remark from a well meaning adult (often a parent) can bring forth a flood of tearful indignation and embarrassment.

I was on a radio phone-in programme once, answering questions about puberty and sexual development, when a mother called to comment that her daughter was experiencing a deep-seated itch in her budding breasts. This was news to me at the time, but it certainly does occur, is not responsive to scratching, and settles as the breasts develop further.

Many girls worry about the size of their breasts. It seems they are either too small, too large, or not growing at the same rate. Yet, in most people, the two sides of the body are never precisely the same. Fortunately, the difference in size generally becomes less obvious the more they grow. Teenage girls need to know that the size and shape of breasts have no relationship whatever to the ability to respond to sexual stimulation, produce milk or feed babies.

Sometimes girls also worry about lumps in their breasts. There are two main types in this age group: single, firm, usually painless lumps that persist (benign fibroadenomas); and multiple, tender areas that vary with the menstrual cycle (fibrocystic lesions). While teenagers should be reassured that these are relatively common and practically never a threat to health, they should be encouraged to practise breast self-examination, a habit that is worth acquiring during adolescence.

Changes in the genital area can also be a source of bewilderment. Pubic hair usually appears around the time that breasts start to develop, although initially it may be difficult to see. In due course, there will be little doubt that it's there, although it can be a bit puzzling when it turns out to be a totally different colour to head hair. Underarm hair usually follows, bringing with it the question of what to do about it, if anything. For girls who find it embarrassing and are prepared to work on it regularly, shaving is the answer. Otherwise, it can simply be left alone.

Occasionally, dark hair forms on the upper lip, on the arms and even around the nipples in some girls, and, although not always welcome, is entirely normal. It is only of medical concern if the appearance of increased or darkened body hair is accompanied by other changes such as a lowered voice, or more severe acne which may suggest the possibility of some hormonal problem.

Then there's the vagina, simple in design but complex in function. Appalled by the degree of ignorance about this extraordinary female body part, one sex educator has dubbed the vagina 'one of the world's best kept secrets'. Not only do many girls, and women, have little idea of exactly what's there, but it may even be regarded with considerable distaste. Parental attitudes conveyed during childhood have a lot to do with this view, and it is also subtly endorsed by tampon advertisers, who emphasise the clean and hygienic applicator that makes insertion 'less messy'. The best way for girls to clarify their understanding of this part of their anatomy is to check it out with a mirror.

Sometimes girls worry about their hymen. They may have heard stories about it, particularly its importance as an indication of virginity. Yet often it is difficult even for doctors to know whether or not it is intact. The hymen consists of a tissue membrane of variable thickness with an opening of variable size. It is usually situated where the vagina begins. Girls may wonder what's likely to happen when intercourse takes place. As a general guide, the more complete the hymen is (sometimes it is merely a remnant) and the smaller the opening, the more force is required to break it. If this is the case, the girl might feel some pain and may bleed a little after first intercourse.

A Sweet Secret

In *The Diary of a Young Girl*, Anne Frank wrote:

> Each time I have a period—and that has been only three times—I have a feeling that in spite of all the pain, unpleasantness, and nastiness, I have a sweet secret, and that is why, although it is nothing but a nuisance to me in a way, I always long for the time that I shall feel that secret in me again.

Such a positive view of this normal and unavoidable aspect of a woman's life is relatively unusual in Western society. Surveys show that many young women view menstruation as a hassle, do not know what the menstrual discharge contains, or more importantly, how it comes about. Parents can protect their daughters from having unwarranted misgivings by discussing menstruation with them, or by providing a book containing simple and explicit information.

Here are some useful facts about adolescent periods:

- Most girls experience their first period (menarche) at around 12 or 13, although it may occur any time between 10 and 16

- A delay in getting started may be due to an inherited tendency, poor nutrition and weight loss (as in anorexia), excessive physical exercise, or a chronic childhood illness
- The first period usually occurs around 2 years or so after breasts have started to develop, and there is a marked slowing of overall growth; a girl will have achieved close to 95 per cent of her adult height
- In a normal period lasting 3 to 5 days, the total discharge is only about 100 ml (about 6 tablespoons) and consists of broken down tissue, blood and a considerable amount of mucous
- Early menstrual cycles are frequently irregular, because the system is still immature and an ovum is not always shed each month; this can last for a year or two before settling down, and rarely requires medical intervention; (it does

not, however, give contraceptive security, as some kids might think)

- Early periods are generally painless, but as the cycle becomes more normalised, premenstrual tension and physical discomforts become more common (painful periods are the commonest cause of lost school and, subsequently, work days in young women)
- A healthy girl can exercise, swim, ride a horse, dance at parties or do anything she likes while she menstruates; a parent who can communicate a positive attitude about periods provides a daughter with a gift for life

During the early stages, having periods takes some getting used to. There are other normal concerns as well. The odour that occurs, for example, when menstrual blood comes in contact with air and airborne bacteria, is something that may worry girls and older women, but this is rarely discussed. It may help to talk about it or at least to reassure your daughter that the odour is perfectly normal and nothing to worry about, even if she feels slightly uncomfortable about it. Washing hands before, as well as after, handling a sanitary towel or tampon is an important rule of hygiene. Teenagers may have heard of 'toxic shock syndrome' and sometimes fear using tampons for this reason. However, if they are changed four or five times a day, handled as little as possible before insertion and not left in overnight (by using a pad instead), the chances of catching this infection are extremely small. The choice of sanitary towel or tampon is an individual decision and is best worked out by letting your daughter use what she feels most comfortable with.

What Happens to Boys?

Unlike the caterpillar whose bizarre bodily changes can take place in total privacy within a cosy cocoon, there is little escape from close and critical scrutiny for the hapless adolescent boy.

For some reason, he is often an object of fun, while the adolescent girl is more likely to be regarded with tenderness.

It's Not Funny

As the larynx grows and vocal cords lengthen, boys acquire a husky voice that 'breaks' a year or so later. (Voice changes occur in girls too, but are less marked.) Not surprisingly, boys seem to see less humour in the situation than others. Later on, the male voice drops an octave or more in pitch, increases in volume and takes on a more even tonal quality.

Another embarrassing development can be breast enlargement in young teenage boys. This is normal and affects many kids; possibly around as many as 80 per cent, and is mostly quite mild. Changing hormones are responsible. It is called gynaecomastia and can be quite alarming, particularly if the boy is not expecting it, or if it progresses beyond the usual small swelling of either or both breasts. A golden haired 16 year old boy I saw had only slightly enlarged breasts but was most distressed about it. In his view, they were 'too full'. He felt they were noticed when he was swimming (a common reason for boys avoiding the water altogether) and was 'wondering if something could be done about it'.

For some boys, fears might even run to, 'Maybe this means I'm gay' or, 'Perhaps I'm turning into a girl'. In most cases, however, it disappears within a year, but if it lasts longer, or is very obvious, it might be worth seeking a professional opinion. Surgery is sometimes considered, especially when psychological stress is great.

Puberty is very much to do with the development of special body hair, and boys are sensitive about this as well. Pubic hair is OK, more or less, because it turns up early and is usually welcome. Underarm hair, on the other hand, is associated with, and actually preceded by, an increase in the size and productivity of sweat glands. Ask any parents about perspiration odour in their adolescent sons, and the pained grimace which follows will tell all.

In comparison to this, upper lip fuzz and wispy chin hairs are innocuous and entertaining, that is, to everyone in the family except the owner of the fuzz. Although a boy might be very tempted to shave this off, the need to shave regularly is unusual before 16 or 17. And last, but not least, chest hair might make an appearance, always late, and despite fervent wishes to the contrary, totally unrelated to strength or virility.

A Continuing Concern

Virility, and a boy's anxieties about it are however, very much related to the size and development of his penis. And, let's face it, boys aren't the only ones to worry about the size of their penises. Not only is it a continuing concern of fully grown men, but also of mothers who take their sons along to the local doctor for reassurance. The mother of one boy I was consulted about was most sceptical of my opinion that all was well with her 12 year old's penis, and that I could see no reason why it should not continue to grow normally. She actually phoned me after she got home (out of earshot of her son, of course), and insisted I repeat the reassurance.

Penises simply differ in size and, although kids sometimes worry about it, size has no bearing on adequate functioning, which is generally the underlying concern. Differences are most obvious when penises are at rest. As pubertal boys can achieve a roaring erection in about 3 seconds flat, it is obviously a mistake for them to check out the competition amongst flaccid organs. Unfortunately, 'Do I shape up compared to the others?' is a question that boys and men tend to ask themselves while standing at a urinal or undressing in a changing room. At some point, males have to reconcile themselves to the fact that there is more to life than being well hung.

More importantly, teenage boys should be encouraged to examine their own testicles. A normal testicle is egg-shaped and somewhat firm to the touch. It should be smooth and free of lumps and should have no unusually sensitive areas. Testicular self-examination (TSE) hasn't really caught on yet, but it is just as necessary as breast self-examination in women.

A Noteworthy Event

A boy's first ejaculation is a remarkable experience and a noteworthy event. It can be as startling as the first period for a girl, and has, of course, exactly the same biological significance, only we tend to discuss it less.

Alfred Kinsey's famous 1948 study of the sexual practices of men, has provided the only available information on how this milestone usually comes about. For two out of three males, the first ejaculation results from masturbation. Some boys will have been practising already for some time and can report the orgasmic sensation known euphemistically as a 'dry run'. Others experience spontaneous emissions of semen.

'Wet dream' is the term used to describe ejaculation of semen that occurs during sleep, but this is not unheard of during the waking hours. (A worried teenager was referred to me once having ejaculated while sitting quietly at a computer.) This release of semen is involuntary. While not all boys have this experience, those who do may find it embarrassing. The important thing to remember is that it is normal. Men produce sperm cells constantly and this is one way the body has of releasing stored semen to make way for new supplies.

Here are a few more facts:

- The consistency of adolescent semen is highly variable and often 'lumpy'
- Sperm are actually present in enormous numbers from the very first ejaculation, even though they make up only a tiny fraction of the volume; there have been many reported cases of pregnancy occurring where the male partner was of a tender age
- Boys who don't know what semen is, invariably imagine the worst, especially if it has appeared in response to their very own (and perfectly normal) efforts; I have seen highly fraught virginal youngsters convinced they had miraculously contracted some sort of sexually transmitted disease

Confusion and misunderstandings about sexual development, for both boys and girls, can produce a lot of unnecessary anxiety.

Open and candid communication between parents and children will go some of the way to avoiding this, if this openness has already been established. But it's difficult if parents are as anxious and embarrassed as their kids and don't know how to raise the subject. Sometimes there is an understanding between parents and children *not* to talk about sexual development. Everyone has their own level of privacy and it's often easier to seek out information from books and magazines rather than to talk directly about it. If this describes you, then leaving a judicious trail of books, magazines and pamphlets which your kids can pick up at their leisure, might be one way of making sure they learn about what's going on. Humour can sometimes help too, which is probably why Peter Mayle's book *What's Happening to Me?* (Macmillan, 1978) has been such a success.

On the Grow

Apart from the first 6 months of life, these few, short years see the fastest rate of growth ever, especially in warm weather. Just before puberty begins, growth actually slows down, as if gearing up for the amazing effort to follow. Then it's on, and before long, that little boy or girl you used to pat affectionately on the head, is nonchalantly lounging on your shoulder. Parents sometimes feel they have entered *Gulliver's Travels*.

Mainly Upwards

Physical growth during puberty is dramatic. It accounts for nearly a quarter of an adult's final height and around half of his or her final weight. This whole process is called the 'growth spurt' and, somewhere along the way, there will be a 12 month period of fastest growth. During this year, a girl can gain up to 8 cm (approximately 3¼ in) in height, and nearly 5 kg (approximately 11 lb) in weight. A boy can gain an amazing 10 cm (around 4 in) in height, and 6 kg (around 13 lb) in weight. No wonder trouser bottoms climb up shins to reveal naked ankles almost every other week!

Girls get started earlier (that's just the way it is), with the onset of the growth spurt generally coinciding with the appearance of breasts. Although boys start later, they have the dubious consolation of growing for longer and ending up taller. Initially, however, particularly around their final year at primary school, the size difference between the sexes is considerable. Following the peak, growth slows down, and except for perhaps a centimetre or so, should be complete by about 18. Then you can look back nostalgically at old photographs and wonder what happened to the cute little kid you once knew.

Some kids take their time getting there, which can be a bit tedious, while others go through it like a rocket, sometimes in as little as 2 years. Of course, adolescents yearn to be average, so being even slightly out of step with one's friends is an uncomfortable experience. Parents need to remember that being the first one to shoot up in height can be as difficult for their daughter or son as being the last to experience their growth spurt.

Too Short

When it comes to physical size, teenagers will have their own ideas about what's OK and what's not. If you were the shortest in the class, you'd be in no doubt at all. Even if most of the others were taller than you, chances are you'd feel too short. Parents sometimes don't realise the extent to which being short affects their children.

The teenage years are the very worst for really short people. One short young man I know has a great talent for making people laugh. He confided in me once that he always goes out of his way to 'clown around. Otherwise,' he said, 'they might laugh at me anyway, and that would be much worse'. Short teenagers are extremely sensitive to stares, curiosity and rude comments. They often have low self-esteem and feel inadequate. According to the research, this is particularly true of boys.

They also find it extremely difficult to hold their own socially, particularly in regard to the opposite sex. While this is true for both boys and girls, it is sometimes harder for boys because of social stereotyping which says boys are supposed to be taller than girls. But it is hard for girls too. It's no fun being treated younger than you are, which can be incredibly aggravating, or to be left out of things. Sadly, very short teenagers sometimes do a lot of staying at home.

There are at least a hundred reasons for a teenager being short and it makes a big difference whether it's permanent or temporary:

Permanently too short—The vast majority of kids who are short by nature usually have parents who are also short, although a chronic illness or genetic disorder is sometimes responsible

Temporarily too short—This is almost always due to delayed puberty: late starters have their growth spurt postponed and, for what can seem like an eternity, are smaller than everyone else; eventually these children come into puberty and end up approximately as tall as their parents, one or both of whom may sometimes have had an identical pattern of development

Whatever the cause, it is an enormous advantage for short teenagers to have well informed parents, friends and teachers. In the first instance, if there is any concern about a child's growth, it is important to get it checked out as something treatable may be responsible, although healthy kids are simply heading for the final height they were meant to be. Those who are slow to develop are often reassured to discover that Mum or Dad had a similar pattern of development. Alternatively, if short stature is due to an inherited form of dwarfism (such as achondroplasia), it is best to consult an expert in the field, as there may be special medical problems to contend with as well.

To be permanently short, of course, is to be faced with problems mostly related to community attitudes. Often the onus falls on you, the parent, to provide reassurance and realistic support; to encourage doing things where physical size and strength are not prerequisites for success and fulfilment; and to point out that there are some very talented and successful short people around (as any die-hard Woody Allen fan would know).

Too Tall

While short stature creates greater problems for boys, excessive tallness provides particular difficulties for girls. Being head and shoulders above your girlfriends is bad enough, but towering over the boys you know (again, because of social stereotyping) is even worse. Tall girls can't hide, although some do stoop and become hunched over, but poor posture does not solve the problem. They still stick out in a crowd. The same is true for tall boys.

The most common reason by far for being tall is having tall parents and tall grandparents. A man of 190 cm (6 ft 3 in), whose wife was 170 cm (5 ft 7 in), was telling me about his tall children. The 13 year old girl was already 180 cm (5 ft 11 in) and still growing (the kids at school called her 'giraffe'); the son, at 10 years of age, was also tall and thin (his nickname was 'spaghetti legs').

'People don't realise the logistical problems involved,' he explained. 'At primary school, long legs don't fit under the desk, at least, certainly not comfortably, and suitably sized clothes and shoes are extremely hard to find.' This Dad, unlike to his own apparently, seemed empathic to his kids' plight. But he encouraged them to accept it. He knew from experience that eventually, the difficulties would seem less serious. This is true. As with many other agonising bodily concerns of adolescence, the passage of time does wonders.

In some situations, such as when it is predicted that a girl will reach a height of greater than 183 cm (6 ft), oestrogen pills can be prescribed to stop her growing. Although there have been no drastic problems with this treatment since it was first introduced in 1956, it is an unsettling idea to interfere in this way with a normal, immature hormonal system. The teenager, her parents and the doctor concerned need to be pretty sure that it's warranted. Efforts to raise self-esteem and encourage pride and acceptance are generally preferable.

A Temporary Mess

It should come as no surprise that physical changes that occur in adolescence make kids look like a house on moving day—a temporary mess! Unfortunately, children in the throes of puberty do look, and often feel, rather ridiculous, mostly because the growth of visible body parts is staggered. This is what happens:

- The head, hands and feet are growing fastest, and reach adult size soonest (which means that Dad might still be able to look down at a kid who's just moved into larger shoes than his)
- The neck, arms and legs follow, and grow significantly faster than the trunk
- The trunk (which includes the spine, obviously), is completed last, eventually making up the major part of increased height gained

There is no physical pain or discomfort involved in all this, but it explains why young adolescents have such an awkward, ungainly and disproportionate appearance. While they're growing fast, however, they may feel relatively helpless and out of control, which makes them extremely sensitive. At some point, it may be impossible to find clothes or shoes to fit as they're just out of children's sizes and not quite into adult clothes (or simply not quite right). You may get to abhor shopping and feel like killing the shop assistants *and* your kid, but it's nobody's fault.

Then there's the face. With an overly prominent nose, a temporarily less prominent chin, and probably a few blackheads for good measure, the overall effect is not going to win first prize in a beauty competition. A pubertal young person is generally not too thrilled about what's happening to the face, and keeps track of it with an almost morbid fascination. After all, practically every time he or she peers into a mirror (which is often), someone new looks back and every little blot or blemish is duly noted. In an Australian study of body image (which is, essentially, the way we think we look), the only people who were able to recognise a photograph of their face upside-down, were young adolescents.

Acne—The Unkindest Physical Change

Acne is often an unavoidable part of growing up, and one of the least pleasant. At some stage, almost three-quarters of all adolescents will experience it to some degree, most mildly. In its more severe forms, acne is both disfiguring and depressing. There are other problems with it as well: much of the advertising about treatments is misleading (which is disillusioning); and most adults (including doctors, I'm afraid) don't take it seriously enough.

When my 11 year old daughter first complained about 'tiny little bumps' on her forehead and cheeks, I could neither see nor feel them. She was adamant, however, not only that they were obvious and unsightly, but also that they warranted immediate medical eradication. Kids don't think it's funny and are very touchy about it. And a slightly older girl who consulted me about something entirely different, surprised me with her comment, 'I've got a few pimples, but they haven't turned into acne yet, thank goodness.' She took it very bravely when I gently explained that they were one and the same. Of course, one can have acne, in the form of blackheads and whiteheads, without having pimples.

Everybody's an expert on this subject, so it's not difficult to get a bit confused yourself. Acne occurs because testosterone, the male sex hormone, which is also secreted in small amounts by girls, affects sebaceous glands, causing the ducts that lead to the surface of the skin to get blocked. At least, that's how the trouble starts.There are some notorious and common misconceptions and it might help to set the record straight:

- Acne is not an infection—the pus is sterile and you cannot catch it from someone, which means that medicated preparations are unnecessary and may even irritate the skin further
- Acne has nothing to do with dirt or pollution and can actually be made worse by too much washing and scrubbing (gentle washing with ordinary, bland soap twice a day is quite sufficient)

- Bad thoughts and 'dirty habits' have nothing to do with why acne occurs, although many teenagers are not too sure about this

- Diet is less crucial than earlier thought: fat eaten in the diet is not excreted through the skin (which has its own separate supply); even the dreaded effects of chocolate are overrated; in a famous study of teenagers using double dose chocolate bars and artificial chocolate bars over a 2 month period (the kids didn't know which was which) there was no difference in the number of pimples produced

A temporary mess

- Despite one's most fervent wish (that special date next Saturday night?), there's no way to get clear skin fast! Acne lesions take their time to develop and, even with the best treatments available (lotions, creams, gels and antibiotics), healing takes a minimum of 4 to 6 weeks; changing medications, often through frustration and impatience, only makes matters worse.

Conclusion

Both teenagers and parents can survive the perils of puberty if they know what's going on. After all, these normal, biological changes have been around for a long time. In many ways, the most difficult part of the whole business is the related feelings and behaviour.

What is most important is that parents are able to encourage their children to greet the changes that occur during puberty with understanding, acceptance and pride. As parents, you may be frequently asked for your opinion about your teenager's appearance, yet when you answer with encouragement get responses such as, 'Yes, but you're my Mum, it looks all right to you'. Your opinions are valued, even if it doesn't seem so at the time, so don't be discouraged.

CHAPTER TWO

Infuriatingly Normal Behaviour

There is nothing quite like adolescent behaviour. Suddenly the sweet, compliant child of recent memory has turned into a moody, rebellious adolescent—and parents certainly don't like it. No other period in a child's life makes them feel so alarmed, angry or indignant, and over what are in essence, trivial and harmless issues. Or are they?

Coping with adolescent ups and downs is never easy. It doesn't help to be told that the behaviour that's driving you up the wall is 'perfectly normal'. But it might help to know that teenagers are generally as puzzled about it as we are.

Maybe It's the Hormones

Even before the earliest signs of puberty have appeared, children are experiencing vague bodily sensations and emotional stirrings related to their changing internal chemistries. Without knowing how or why, they start to feel different and unsettled, which is exactly how they seem to others.

It's an attractive idea actually, to blame the hormones for all moody behaviour and emotional outbursts as something has to account for it. But it is not very well understood. Rising levels of

Infuriatingly normal behaviour

male sex hormones (mostly testosterone) are certainly responsible for the marked increase in the sex drive which is such a feature of adolescence and there is proven evidence of the effect of hormonal changes in regard to premenstrual tension in girls. Beyond that is speculation.

Ups and Downs

Whatever the causes, the teenage years are a time of extreme sensitivity and, particularly during the early stages, literally anything (or nothing) can spark off a mood swing. Living with a teenager has been accurately likened to riding a roller coaster of emotional ups and downs. An apparently happy and confident kid can suddenly lash out angrily, or become painfully self-conscious or despairingly pessimistic. Sometimes there is an undercurrent of irritability, while at other times, life is just great, and nothing is too much trouble.

As ghastly as the miseries can be, bursts of unbridled euphoria are also hard to take (not that one would be so unkind as to complain). It's puzzling when a recently miserable teenager suddenly radiates light and love or prances around loudly extolling the virtues of life. Noisy, continuous giggling at something that seems patently unfunny to the adult mind or loud yahoos when the football team has won can also really get on your nerves.

During these years teenagers need time to be alone. They need 'time out' to quietly ponder momentous questions to do with becoming an individual, such as, 'Who am I?', 'Who will I become?' or 'What should I believe in?' This may mean a physical retreat to the bedroom, or other private place, or merely an unwillingness to talk. The latter provides a sort of psychological privacy, as in, 'Absolutely nothing happened at school today'.

Psychologists call this process 'introspective withdrawal' and consider it extremely important. Some interesting research used long range beepers to discover what teenagers were doing and how they were feeling at different points in the day. This revealed that young people are often melancholy while they're alone but, after a while, their mood lightens, as if they've been emotionally refurbished by the experience.

What is one supposed to do in response to these emotional

carryings on? Giving in to frustration and tearing out your hair may be one way to go, but kids don't seem to understand that. Nor does seeking an instant explanation work. You are liable to get the 'leave me alone, stop bugging me' response. Perhaps the best that parents can do is not get too uptight. If we can stand by without intruding, sympathetically underreact and go easy on the heavy advice, the whole situation can remain manageable. Well, that's the theory. Relationships between parents and teenagers cannot always remain calm, even if that's how you might want them to be. A lot depends on the nature and extent of the aggravation.

Fidgets and Fiddles

Why can't teenagers keep still? They are so much and so often on the go, that early adolescence has been dubbed 'the age of movement'. It's most obvious when they're together. A collection of 12 and 13 year olds, for example, is a twitching, twittering mass of arms and legs (which, as you'll recall, are the body parts that lengthen relatively early in puberty). Constant movement is usually accompanied by animated talking, giggling and raucous laughter. Catch a morning train or bus on any school day and you'll recognise the scene. Or watch how often teenagers walk in and out of the house, opening doors, closing doors, slamming doors, letting them squeak. Kids just have to be on the go and the house has to move in time with them.

The most plausible explanation for this is a build up of energy and tension (some of it due to hormones for sure) that has to go somewhere. This is one reason why physical activity such as vigorous dancing and sweaty sports, are such healthy and necessary outlets for teenagers.

Of course, outdoor cavorting is one thing. For mums and dads, the problem is mainly when exuberant kids are stuck indoors. That's when not only the fidgets, but also the fiddles (the need to constantly touch things) really take their toll. Boys appear to be somewhat worse than girls in this regard and also more clumsy. Practically nothing within reach is safe from detailed scrutiny and handling. When this scourge of so called 'manipulative restlessness' is upon them, breakages and spills become a routine part of life. (A teenager I know can carefully pour milk *next to the cup*, each and every time.)

Stay cool, the experts say. Expressing your true feelings about the oil-based paint that has just been 'accidentally' slopped all over the kitchen floor, will only damage their fragile young egos. Oh well. And what about when kids do incredibly irritating things, over and over again? Bizarre facial grimaces or frenzied hyena impersonations at dinner, for example, can really get you down, especially after a bad day. You can end up wondering if your previously docile child has gone completely mad. Or is it merely intended to do that to you?

Realistically, with fidgets and fiddles, yelling and nagging don't seem to help very much. Even a quiet and friendly request to 'please stop it' will rarely work instantly (a few more of 'whatever it is' are needed, you see, to save face). Some parents get so stirred up by all this, that they seek professional advice, usually with disappointing results. Someone is certain to say, 'Don't worry about it, it's only infuriatingly normal behaviour; it'll pass.' Meanwhile, the idea of setting up a tent in the back garden and sending the kid out to live in it, may become increasingly attractive.

Don't Bug Me—I'm Rebelling

You know that it's supposed to happen; you've heard about it, read about it, and probably even been personally warned about it; but when it's actually happening, it's not much fun—Teenage Rebellion. It can take many forms, from ordinary ingratitude and disdain (which are irritating, even if they are part of a healthy striving for independence), to more outrageous and sometimes frankly dangerous behaviour.

Conformity has been described as 'what you do to keep your folks off your back while you're making up your mind what you really want to do'. Doing things *differently* is what becoming a separate, mature person is all about. There's no other way. Who'd want an adolescent to be constantly amenable and passive? It might be nice, but it wouldn't be normal.

Messy Bedrooms

Benjamin Franklin coined the phrase, 'a place for everything and everything in its place'. It's a deceptively simple idea and probably the source of endless conflict in millions of homes around the world.

Actually, some teenagers are fastidiously neat. (Don't knock it, it saves your vocal cords.) Not my daughter! From time to time, her bedroom contains the following, all visible to the naked eye: knotted, unwashed clothing (not all hers); twisted wet towels; assorted paper, pens and other implements of study; apple cores, lolly wrappers, cups, dishes and other evidence of midnight snacks; sporting equipment, magazines, cosmetics and loads of other essential teenage paraphernalia. (What's stuck on the walls is another story!)

If there's one thing that infuriates parents, it's a messy bedroom. Not just a moderately untidy one perhaps, but the sort you'd have to see to believe. In terms of gnawing aggravation, a proper messy bedroom can win hands down over many other rebellious adolescent behaviours such as: the pouty, resentful expression (recognised in most households as 'that face'); the viciously wilful procrastinations; or the ever-so-careless (but really quite studied) disregard for living room furniture and general decorum.

How negotiable should a messy bedroom be? A teenage photography freak I know suggested this to his parents, 'If you make my bedroom into a darkroom, I promise to keep it tidy'. Not a bad try. There are two main schools of thought:

- Parents have a right to enjoy their own homes (which becomes difficult if one of the bedrooms appears to have been converted, without a building permit, into an indoor piggery). Kids may argue that their room has nothing to do with you. According to the 'Parents' Charter', however, 'a glance at the signature on the cheques that pay the bills will prove otherwise'.
- Alternatively, teenagers have a right to wallow in their own mess; 'It's my mess and I love it', so why not let it be their problem? The door can always be kept closed.

Seeking the middle ground will probably get you a decent clean up once a week. Surely that's not too much too ask? Meanwhile, some specific limits can be set. In our house, for example, we're more troubled by collections of mouldy old food and knotted wet towels than by general untidiness. I also find it particularly irksome that a desk provided for study purposes is piled high with junk while the student sits cross-legged on the floor, in poor light, trying to work. But in the interests of international peace I let that one pass. You probably need to work out a level of messiness (or tidiness) that you can tolerate, that is, books and sporting equipment on the floor but not dirty plates or clothes left in the room for longer than a day (or however long you can bear it).

The Art of Negotiation: Turn Down the Radio or I'll Kill You

Adults rarely like their kids' tastes in music and entertainment or how they like to dress and wear their hair. But most parents understand that they need to have at least some freedom of expression and room to discover their individuality. Teenagers also need symbols that their world is different from that of their parents, and if shocking Mum and Dad is part of it, so much the better. Styles may change, but the basic idea flows from generation to generation.

There's nothing new about loud music. Anyone who grew up in the 1960s knows all about it. Of course, in their new found wisdom, parents are aware that prolonged exposure to ear splitting cacophony can wreck your hearing. Do kids care? Not at all. Teenage music has to be loud: it's a way to prove you're alive, it's a way to tune out the world (almost fool-proof these days, with walkman radios and cassette players). What poses the greatest threat to parental sanity, however, is the bone-shattering beat bursting from the bedroom. The explanation that this is an essential aid to study, doesn't quite work.

For a teenager, clothing and hairstyle are intensely personal and important ways of identifying yourself as an individual and as part of a group. Most young people spend a lot of time on their appearance, not only feeling anxious about being normal, but also on hair and makeup, dressing and shopping. When you're stuck in a school uniform all week, dressing up allows you to be creative and to feel more confident. Sometimes, it's simply that you like the way something looks.

A 14 year old girl who came to see me had a bizarre, multi-coloured hairdo, quite different, as it happened, from any of her friends. It made her look as if she'd just been electrocuted. I asked her why she did it, and she explained, 'I know it looks crazy, but at least there's something special about me.' I remember another teenager, a 16 year old boy with stringy, shoulder length hair, who burst into tears while telling me that his mother wouldn't even walk with him on the same side of the street. (And some poor kids have parents who insist on walking with them on the same side of the street!)

We get terribly upset about these trappings of youth, in the same way, no doubt, that our parents were stirred by the hippie styles of the 1960s. More recently, many young people were impressed with the punk look, although relatively few went the whole way. Short, spiky, even brightly coloured hair became fashionable, rather than anti-fashion, as it was when the punk culture first emerged in the mid 1970s. Of course, the unsavoury, hostile, dedicatedly self conscious punk with studs, torn singlets, swastikas and safety pin jewellery was very much out to repulse and shock. (A recent American study found that punks are very conscious of the image they create and rather like being viewed as society's misfits or outcasts.)

Once again, the secret is to underreact. The teenagers whose parents are able to view their 'interesting get-ups', or desire to try them out, with bemused understanding, and even refuse to see it as a problem, are doing well. But the whole thing falls apart when 'oldies' go too far and try to emulate these youthful styles themselves. How are you supposed to 'do your own thing' if Mum or Dad are desperately trying to look the same as you? It's indecent. Generally, the two generations know their place. Perhaps it should occur to us, when we're complaining about our odd looking kids, that they might not be too impressed with how we look either. If we're lucky, they'll be too polite to say so!

Creeps Are Other People's Children

Human beings are gregarious by nature, but of all age groups, adolescents have the most powerful urge to belong, to be one of the gang. Few parents do not recognise, and at times fear, the powerful influence of the peer group.

For adolescents, friends and acquaintances provide safety in numbers. They provide an antidote to uncertainty and reassurance in the face of the common foe (you know who that is). Going along with the crowd, even if only in innocuous matters such as dress, signals a distancing from parental influence, although knowing that this is normal, doesn't necessarily make it less scary for you. Yet it is often the kid without friends, the social isolate, who is a cause for concern.

At the very least, you may view your teenager's friends as 'the blind leading the blind', although it is best not to openly denigrate them as it only makes things worse. At the very worst, you may wonder, 'Are those creeps really leading my nice kid astray?', in which case it's somewhat harder to know what to do.

Organised groups like Scouts, Guides or the youth club are more or less to our liking, mostly because they actively set out to build good characteristics such as brotherhood, tolerance, responsibility, cleanliness and leadership. Young people who turn their nose up at these mostly adult supervised, leisure time youth groups, do so, they say, because they find them rigid, boring or out of date. Even the harmless, social, relatively loosely formed teenage group, does not engender overly strong parental feelings one way or another. They are usually viewed by parents as neutral and nothing special.

On the other hand, there are a number of teenage groups that get parents very worried, namely those that are less than mindful of accepted values and social norms:

Religious cults—These are characterised by their insistence on mental bondage, absolute obedience to a charismatic (and invariably male) leader, and extreme separation from parents; teenage girls with low self-esteem are particularly vulnerable to being caught up in them

Street gangs—Those young people who, for one reason or another, have to go it alone in the world and find support and companionship by banding together; while these 'tough kids' can teach you and me a great deal about survival, it's when they deface public property, steal cars and terrorise innocent passers by that we don't like them, this is 'destructive rebellion' in anybody's language

Risk taking groups—Not necessarily 'bad' or delinquent kids (although they may be included) who get caught up in dares to do dangerous things; drug taking can start out this way

The fears parents have about such groups and the possibility of their kids becoming involved with them are not unreasonable. But you can't keep teenagers locked up. What you can do is try to keep track of things and say what you think if you have reason to be alarmed. Of course, while young people are exercising a choice in the company they keep, sometimes they are pushed into the arms of 'unsavoury customers' by what's happening at home. An inhospitable, stressful or dangerous household, for example, is something they will want to react against anyway. Seeking bad company may be the way they choose to do it.

Speaking in defence of youth, a teenage girl I spoke to indignantly stated, 'You know, adults have peer group pressure too, but that's all right because it's colleagues, not just useless hooligans'. She went on to explain that 'Sometimes groups are brought together because they are all the ones the "nice" kids call weirdos'. Clearly there are lots of non-sinister reasons for being part of a group.

Even under normal circumstances, dealing with adolescent rebellion is the supreme test for parents. This is where you need to have a credible track record in regard to establishing clear guidelines, providing a good example, and being willing to allow your own values and opinions to be challenged while sticking to your guns. Some of the groundwork will have been established during the pre-adolescent years. Becoming loudly angry or sullenly silent will not eradicate testing behaviour, while quiet discussion, even when opinions differ strongly, still remains the best way to keep lines of communication open.

Becoming loudly angry or sullenly silent will not eradicate testing behaviour

'Wasting Time'

Adults have their ideas about what represents good use of time and teenagers have theirs. Not surprisingly, they're rather different. Those activities which seem designed specifically to aggravate parents include: daydreaming, spending hours on the telephone, and just hanging around.

Daydreaming

Young adolescents have an uncanny way of blocking out anything that interferes with their pursuit of happiness. They lose things, are generally forgetful and infuriatingly absent minded. Losing track of time is understandable (and forgiveable), particularly when they're having fun, but vacant expressions and vacuous behaviour take a bit more explaining. As an anonymous young graffitiist wrote,'I live in a world of my own, but visitors are welcome'.

During puberty, children start to gain new intellectual abilities. This enables them to generate and explore hypotheses, make deductions, and achieve higher order abstractions or, more simply, they become able to ponder about such things as the miracle of thought and the meaning of life. An important manifestation of this is *daydreaming*, which can make kids look completely spaced out.

Parents and teachers know a lot about this and it drives them crazy. As one teacher commented in a school report, 'Jason spends a lot of time contemplating matters other than those immediately to hand'. Of course, teenagers do not find this in any way strange. One rather mature young person explained, 'Let's face it. Most kids' lives are not what they could be. Especially at school.' In any case, all that is happening is the normal thinking process.

Adolescent daydreams have no simple story. They're often disjointed and vague, sometimes romantic or heroic, sometimes sinister or vicious. They are important, however, in several different ways:

- Adolescents try out different behaviours in their imaginations without having to face the hazards of the real world (erotic fantasies would come into this category)
- They can mentally plan ahead and thus gain motivation and confidence
- Daydreaming also provides a temporary escape from the stresses of everyday life (and who'd blame them for that?)

Get Off the Bloody Telephone

From a parent's point of view, teenagers and telephones are bad news. Kids can happily chat, giggle or whisper for hours on end, unless you're determined to take a firm hand. Late night calls, early morning calls, escalating phone bills, mounting frustration, and the humiliation of friends dropping in to check on your health because they've being trying to get through for days, are all part of the picture.

Teenagers on the phone are poetry in motion, never still for more than a few seconds and assuming practically every position a human body is capable of. As I have discovered first hand, they will go to extraordinary lengths to obtain privacy. (Have you ever been confronted by a 'talking blob' under a blanket?) When I was on call for the hospital once, I bought an extension cord but had to give it away because to find the phone became a veritable treasure hunt.

Why do young people need to spend so much time on the phone? There are probably several reasons. Having an instant connection with the outside world, when one is temporarily confined to the house, is one—clearly a matter of life and death. Sometimes it is simply a matter of getting help with homework that's too difficult for parents.

More importantly, however, it's a way to check out what friends and acquaintances are thinking and doing. This is usually done with a tone of contrived triviality, so that no one knows what you're doing. It also keeps you in touch with what the group is up to. Talking on the phone is a way to have a private conversation with a special friend—certainly at school, kids don't get a lot of privacy. Also, when the time comes, it is a valuable aid to romance, as it allows intimacy at a safe distance and give-away body language remains private.

Like everything else, a teenager's use or abuse of the telephone may be normal, but that doesn't mean it's not infuriating. One knowing teenager wondered if some parents 'get really stupid about telephone socialising, because they feel shut out'. Interesting thought.

Nevertheless, for parents who simply cannot turn a blind eye (after all, somebody important may be trying to get in touch with you), some sort of strategy is called for. A reasonable limit on the number or length of calls may need to be negotiated. Our four kids all make and receive important calls, so we've had to try to work out the fairest system. Even with a limit of two after school calls per person and a 10 to 15 minute maximum, things get extremely congested and the system breaks down at times.

Smaller families may not find this such a problem at all. But for those who do, there are occasions when you may want to consider more definitive action. My personal research has unearthed a range of options that parents have been driven to: give 5 minutes' notice and then pull the plug, buy another phone with a silent number, have the existing one disconnected, invest in a long range beeper, or make kids pay for their own calls (although it's probably your money anyway). Good luck.

Mooching Around

Just hanging around with friends and 'doing nothing much' is typical teenage behaviour, but again, not exactly what most adults would consider a constructive use of time. The importance young people give to it is obvious. After all, simply being together in groups is what teenage social life is all about. Aimless and usually harmless 'mooching around', whether at a shopping centre or in a coffee shop, is a pastime they enjoy immensely. In fact, what kids do is often totally lacking in direction and purpose.

Does it matter? Well, probably not, except that parents want to know what their kids are up to. So they can't help asking, 'Where are you going? Who with? How will you get there and back? What time will you be home?' Sometimes, the best that

Mooching around

honest teenagers can offer is, 'We haven't quite decided what we're doing yet—I'll let you know and keep in touch'. Young people find it hard to justify their need for privacy and intimacy with friends, and it troubles them at times that parents think, 'What are they hiding?'

The sympathetic and perhaps realistic way to view this mooching around behaviour is that young people have only a few short years to have some fun (money, transport and opportunity permitting) before the responsibilities of work, families and households descend on them. Naturally kids want to enjoy themselves and they know how to do that, their way.

Conclusion

There's no way to avoid being amused, irritated or even outraged by the way normal teenagers carry on. We may be tempted to think that there are other things really worth worrying about such as pregnancy, drug and alcohol use or dangerous driving, and we'd be quite right.

Sometimes, however, the very constancy of coping with the daily grind can really wear you down. Sometimes, your only salvation is to have a sense of humour, compare notes with friends, so you'll know you're not suffering alone, or take a break somewhere where teenagers are off limits. It doesn't hurt to remember also, that underneath much infuriatingly normal behaviour there is a thoroughly confused kid. He or she may be silently saying, 'Please understand folks, I'm really a nice person inside'.

CHAPTER THREE

Sexuality—A Sensitive Issue

Where teenagers and sex are concerned, parents worry a lot. They worry that they'll have sex too soon, or with the wrong people or of the wrong kind or not at all. At a slightly less dramatic level, they worry that their kids might be sexually exploited or, alternatively, that they are taking too long to get interested in the opposite sex.

Whether or not adults are comfortable with the idea (mostly they're not), teenagers are sexual beings. Sexuality is an integral and inescapable part of living. It is a vital and important, if somewhat confusing, part of growing up. It should concern us, and not just because there are risks involved.

Why Are Young People Confused?

Why not? Everybody else is. In no other area of human need and activity are there so many mixed messages and catch 22s as there are about sexuality. Previous generations more or less accepted a 'birds and bees' approach (otherwise known as an 'ostrich' approach) to sex. Today, young people are frequently confronted with both their own uncertainty and also that of their adult mentors. Clearly, this makes the task of sorting out their sexuality all the more difficult.

Three obvious sources of confusion are: changing sex roles, the double standard, and 'middle class morality'.

BOOZE
DRUGS
SCANDAL
PASSION
PREGNANCY
SEX
STD's
CRIME
ORGY
RAPE
ABORTION
SEDUCTION
EXPLOITATION
PORNOGRAPHY
PROSTITUTION
GOOD GRIEF!! She should be on the PILL!!
The gang from school are having an all night party at the boat house - can I go?
Another young AIDS victim died today!
SCHOOL SEX SCANDAL

Changing Sex Roles

As early as 3 or 4 years of age, children have not only decided which sex they belong to but have also learned something of the behaviour expected of that sex. We are born either male or female as a result of purely genetic and biological factors. How masculine or feminine we feel and behave, however (which is what 'gender' means), depends on how we are treated by our parents and by what we see and hear going on around us. This process of identification is pretty powerful. Even subtle messages and clues taken in as a young child, have a major influence on our self-concept and behaviour.

Things hot up at adolescence. Consider the different sorts of publications targeted at teenagers. Girls' magazines and novels are loaded with romantic pap, usually with just a hint of sex at the end. The overriding message is that happiness is a thing called boys and there is a lot of advice on how to attract them. Boys' magazines, on the other hand, are also about boys or men, all doing something tough. The emphasis is on action, achievement and hardware. And while, in reality, happiness is also a thing called girls, they're not encouraged to admit it, so of course, they don't, a pattern which sets them up for life.

Sex role stereotypes are alive and well. At the same time, new sorts of role modelling are appearing too. At home, for example, an increasing number of men are starting to pull their weight more with domestic and parenting chores, while women are taking on professional careers. In the world of popular heroes, on the other hand, rock stars who are tantalising 'gender benders' tell a different story. No wonder kids are confused.

The Double Standard

This is so entrenched and so well known that not much needs to be said about it. It's not fair and it's not right, but in the game of love, girls get the worst deal by far. Parents (often fathers) are more suspicious and more controlling of their daughters for a start, and probably always will be, simply because the daughters have more to lose if things go wrong (namely, an unwanted pregnancy). This is not their only problem. Amongst young people themselves, there is a ruthless double standard that works like this:

- Teenage girls come under a lot of sexual pressure from teenage boys, who are also under pressure from other boys, because it's masculine to 'score'
- But they're 'damned if they do, and damned if they don't' as sexually active girls are regarded as 'sluts' by both boys and girls, and those who don't come across are 'frigid' or 'teasers'
- Yet it's supposedly OK for boys to have as much sex as they want! Apparently, they still haven't worked out, or don't want to work out, the basic contradiction in this—who are they going to have all this sex with?
- There is also considerable pressure from friends for girls to talk and act sexually, but this must stop once they have committed themselves to a relationship
- An unfortunate outcome of all this is that boys are almost always less experienced than they say, while girls are at risk of becoming more experienced than they might want

Middle Class Morality

Parents of today's adolescents have seen the most dramatic changes in sexual knowledge, attitudes and behaviour of all time: Dr Alfred Kinsey's amazing exposés about sexual activity in the late 1940s and early 1950s; the advent of the pill, the women's movement and gay liberation in the 1960s; and the crumbling of censorship and the rise of casual sex in the 1970s.

Now, among other things, we have: 'video nasties' which are overly accessible pornography providing a diet of humourless, mechanical, degrading or violent sex which is hardly beneficial for young and impressionable minds, or ours either; discussions of oral sex and the 'G' spot on radio talk shows; openness about homosexuality; the AIDS scare; and a tarnishing of the glorified image of casual sex.

No doubt, much of this change towards greater openness has been for the better, but we are still left with a basic dilemma. In Western society at least, there is no longer a consensus on the issue of premarital chastity, although this remains important in some religious and most ethnic communities. In general, the ideal of the virgin bride has been abandoned, and young people are being increasingly pressured to be sexual. They are bom-

barded with sexual images and innuendoes in virtually every form of media at our disposal.

Alongside these more permissive social attitudes however, there is an enduring middle class morality that takes the opposite line. Most adults have misgivings about the whole issue of adolescent sexuality or frankly disapprove of it. The message kids are getting from the adult world is 'be sexy but also be good' and the nett result, for many, is uncertainty, guilt and stress. Perhaps those teenagers who figure out that there is real value, and safety, in taking it slowly, have a somewhat easier time.

From Giggles to Romance

My youngest son wanted to wear his fanciest clothes to a girl's birthday party. Why? 'Because she loves me', he explained. 'Isn't she too young to be loving boys?', my wife innocently asked. 'Of course not', he replied, 'she's my age—6!' We wonder what lies ahead.

As puberty approaches, children become intensely curious about sex. With eager delight and giggling apprehension they share their fantasies with each other and actively search out information wherever they can find it; in magazines and novels, medical books, dictionaries and encyclopaedias. 'What must a sexual experience be like?', they wonder. 'Where on earth do people put their legs?'

Later on, some of the distortions, rumours and wild tales that filter down from above get sorted out. But with puberty in full swing, there are other things to cope with. Put together an anxious preoccupation with bodily changes and hypersensitivity, and sexuality becomes the emotional minefield of early adolescence.

First infatuations occur at this time (say 11 or 12) and involve strong, new feelings. This is the stuff of romantic daydreams and may be directed at either sex. Nobody else might know about them and kids get over them quickly. Of greater concern to parents are the close relationships that form between young adolescents of the same sex, and the experimental sex play that often goes along with this. (Stories about groups of boys seeing who can ejaculate the furthest are true.) This is a way to learn about physical sensations at a time when the opposite sex is pretty threatening. It is usually a passing phase and helps pave the way for later heterosexual relationships.

It goes without saying that adolescence and masturbation are related. For many parents and kids, however, this remains an area of discomfort. Myths and fantasies abound and, although many young people take it in their stride, others experience guilt, anxiety and shame. Some boys think that they are only given a certain number of ejaculations and if they use them all up in this way, bad luck! Girls may feel guilty about touching 'down there' or may not even know that masturbation provides a multitude of ways in which they can gain sexual pleasure for themselves, simply because they have more erogenous zones than boys.

Masturbation offers some advantages. These include: the release of tension; the lack of any ill effects (it is not possible to masturbate to excess); its safety, in terms of not being able to catch anything; and the way it helps kids to know and understand their bodies and their strong sexual feelings. If parents can communicate that it's OK, if that's what they think, it can be an enormous burden off a teenager's mind.

Parents usually become more anxious about what their teenagers are up to sexually during the middle years of around 14 to 16. This is the time when they are starting to act so grown up but, to you, they still seem so young and immature. There is increasing contact with the opposite sex during these years, which initially takes place within the relative safety of mixed groups (not that kids aren't anxious about it too). I say 'relative safety' because in no way does this preclude a good deal of affectionate, sexual interaction. Sensible kids won't say a lot about this, but as a guess, innocuous sounding middle class activities like 'video parties' are merely comfortable, home based 'tickle and grope' sessions. The settings may have changed somewhat, but parents can remember what they got up to in their teens. What better reason to worry?

When a mother returned home to find her 15 year old daughter sitting, red eyed and stunned, in the middle of her bedroom floor, the first guess was correct—the shattered girl had just broken up with her boyfriend. Where there's love there's trauma. As part of a general sexual awakening, there is a major likelihood of romantic, emotional attachments occurring at this time. They are characteristically short lived. But being head over heels in love involves feelings of desperate ecstasy, or ecstatic desperation, that may never be experienced in as intense a way again. Those who have survived such relationships are not sorry about this at all, because they are exhausting, bewildering and frequently bruising, for both kids and parents.

For adolescents, getting older generally means becoming more sensible and level headed. In the later teens, having a 'good sort' at your side is less important than sharing interests and establishing some give and take. Relationships are likely to be longer term and to involve mutual caring and loyalty, a reasonable setting for the more serious expression of sexual needs. Older teenagers, whose identities are becoming more secure, are also in better shape to cope with the emotions and responsibilities involved.

Going 'All the Way'

The evidence suggests that more teenagers are having sex. Approximately one out of every two adolescents is now said to have had sexual intercourse by 17 or 18 years of age, with no significant difference between boys and girls. This also means that half of them have not yet 'done it' and, for many of those who have, this may have been only once or twice.

Contrary to common belief, teenagers are not promiscuous. Casual sex is rare, and with rampant STDs it's likely to become increasingly so. Most sexually active teenagers have intercourse infrequently and relatively few have intercourse with more than one or two partners.

Studies in Australia and elsewhere give us a more detailed profile. Young people from well to do families who attend private schools (and particularly if they also attend church) are less sexually active than other teenagers, especially those who are out of school and unemployed; country teenagers are less sexually active than their city peers; more adolescent virgins than non-virgins feel closer to, better understood by and have easier communication with their parents, who are also more likely to have discussed sexual matters with them!

The First Time

Before looking at the whys and wherefores, here are some facts about first intercourse:

- The age of first intercourse has become younger (around 15 or 16)
- In about 50 per cent of cases it is planned, possibly more often by the boy
- First intercourse has a seasonal tendency with, for obvious reasons, a peak in the summer
- For girls, male partners tend to be teenagers themselves (common wisdom suggests that if a 15 year old girl has a 19 year old boyfriend, at some point, intercourse is inevitable)
- First intercourse may occur literally anywhere, but often at home—her place or his (yes, parents go out, leaving the house reliably vacant at an opportune time)
- First intercourse rarely comes up to expectations, particularly for girls; in fact, it may happen so quickly (usually in silence, in darkness and without preliminaries) that it is difficult for some girls to know if they've had it at all; it's quite unlikely for girls to have an orgasm either
- Afterwards, not surprisingly, girls are more likely to experience feelings of anxiety, worry, guilt and embarrassment, while boys are more likely to report being excited, satisfied and happy (at least, that's what they say)
- Fewer than 10 per cent of adolescents use any sort of contraception; as staggering as it sounds, 20 per cent of girls become pregnant within 1 month, 50 per cent within 6 months
- When first intercourse is related to incest or rape, the emotional consequences are disastrous

A Question of Readiness

You cannot forbid sexual behaviour in teenagers. This part of growing up is private and you are not going to be around when it happens. This is definitely an emotive subject and parents tend to have differing ideas and feelings. They may think that adolescence is the golden age of sexual growth and that such opportunities to learn by experience will never come again. Other parents, perhaps the majority, think that kids are too immature and irresponsible to have sexual intercourse and that the potential consequences are too devastating.

Alternatively, parents may accept that adolescents have to learn to cope with personal relationships and negotiate the sexual component within them, which may eventually include intercourse. There is much food for thought here, but individual teenagers and their situations vary greatly. Some handle sexual involvement without undue stress while others find themselves totally out of their depth. The earlier they start, of course, the greater the likelihood of bad experiences, and the impact of these can be very enduring. One's fervent hope is that a young person will have thought it through beforehand and had the opportunity to talk about it with somebody sensible.

Who's 'somebody sensible'? Possibly not Mum or Dad. I recently found our old copy of Alex Comfort's *The Joy of Sex* (Mitchell Beazley, 1986) lying open on our bedroom floor. 'Somebody in our family's getting educated' I thought, as I returned it to the shelf. It's not easy to broach the subject of sexual intercourse with your kids and sometimes you can feel very uncomfortable about it. In many families, it's often easier to leave such things unstated and, ironically, this is often what teenagers would prefer. Have you ever tried to bring it up and heard, 'Good grief Mum, I know all that'. There are, of course, more subtle ways to deal with it (by the high quality literature we hide around the house, for instance.)

Why Do They Do It?

In the Australian National Times of April 1981, Adele Horin described intercourse in these terms:

> For teenage boys with racing hormones, the process of intercourse is quick and explosive, an awesome, out of control rush to orgasm. It will never be as quick or driven at any other time in their lives. For many young girls, this rip roaring intercourse is a terrible disappointment . .

So, why do girls go along with it? The submissive role that females have been conditioned to accept is part of it, or she might simply not want to hurt his feelings. There are many lines, however, that girls should not fall for. As Sol Gordon, a leading sex educator, has point out, no boy has ever died from not having an orgasm, however much heavy breathing he can muster.

Being in love is probably the single most important basis for self-justification, as well as making it a potentially more pleasant and pleasurable experience.

For a lot of young people, unfortunately, sex and drugs are related. Both are trendy and involve pressure from friends. Having sex when drunk or under the influence of dope is not uncommon. Other reasons are to do with psychological needs and put young women in particular at great risk. Intercourse can be an effort to gain affection denied by parents, a form of rebellion, or a cry for help. Promiscuous sexual behaviour in girls can be a manifestation of depression, a way to get close to someone, even if briefly, when they're feeling low.

'It Can't Happen to Me'

When it comes to using birth control, sexually active young people are dismal failures. Whether or not they are showing increased responsibility in other areas of their lives, there is some sort of block about it. They generally know about the risks of unwanted pregnancy, and at least something about what's available to prevent it. But certain myths and ideas get in the way, as listed here:

- Sexual relations should be held under natural, spontaneous and unplanned conditions; you don't plan to have sex
- 'It can't happen to me' or 'I'm too young to get pregnant'
- Contraceptives are too troublesome and inconvenient; they interfere with sexual pleasure (a common complaint boys make about condoms)
- Contraceptives are unnatural or potentially harmful to the body and they're too expensive
- Parents might discover such incriminating evidence at home
- It's embarrassing to ask for contraception and thus declare that you are, or intending to become, sexually active
- Contraception is a female responsibility (a belief representing a common and unfortunate cop out for boys)

Even if we were able to remove all these impediments to taking proper precautions, contraceptive usage in the young might not substantially go up, simply because risk taking, so much a part of adolescence, enhances the thrill of guilty pleasures. It's a difficult issue and quite a challenge for parents and other sex educators to tackle. However, contraception is something that parents should talk to their teenagers about, because it's so vital. We want our sons and daughters to be protected from grief. We might merely make them aware that Family Planning clinics exist. Of course, not everybody would be as blunt as the mother who announced to her kids, 'Your father keeps his condoms in the drawer next to the bed. Nobody's counting'.

Not Everybody's Heterosexual

Few parents would be overjoyed to discover that a son or daughter is gay. In our culture, this is not an easy path to follow. Fears of homosexuality cause fathers and mothers to behave in certain ways towards their children, for example, fathers discouraging dressing up and dolls for little boys or mothers limiting their affection for fear of 'making him queer'. Throughout the school years and beyond, any male who doesn't quite fit the stereotyped image of masculinity is at risk of being labelled one of a number of terms of utmost derision. With girls, on the other hand, because our society is more accepting of physical demonstrativeness between females, there is somewhat less consternation about it.

This is a complex subject and, with the AIDS crisis in full swing, one of growing concern. Most teenagers worry about their sexual identity and about their ability to attract and perform sexually with the opposite sex. At some time or other, most will wonder whether or not they are homosexual. Having crushes on the same sex, whether it's a best friend or a class teacher, is very much a normal part of growing up.

Here are some relevant facts:

- Homosexuality is defined as a predominant and persistent preference for sexual arousal by individuals of the same sex plus absent or weak arousal by the opposite sex

- It is currently believed that one's sexual orientation is determined early in life and is not amenable to cure
- The notion of 'gay' or 'straight' is too black or white; there is a spectrum of sexual orientation with most people falling somewhere between the two extremes
- Between 25 and 50 per cent of adolescents are said to have a homosexual experience; (this is *not* homosexuality, but can subsequently cause anxiety in regard to future sexual adjustment)
- The occasional attraction to a person of the same sex is also *not* homosexuality, but can be extremely troubling and very difficult to raise and seek reassurance about
- Adolescent and older homosexual men and lesbians can often date their suspicions to primary school, the clues being a predilection for erotic fantasy about friends of the same sex, and not being attracted to the opposite sex when peers are becoming besotted
- Gay adolescents feel different, that is 'not straight', but for a long time, struggle alone with uncertainty, confusion and fear ('if anyone were to find out, I'd die'); there is frequently low self-esteem and a sense of being a second class citizen
- Young homosexuals are reticent to 'come out' and greatly fear confronting their parents; it comes as an enormous relief to meet other gay people and share needs and concerns, although unhappiness can be ongoing

When the subject of a young person's homosexuality is ultimately broached with parents, there's no way for it not to be a shock. As this is not what they wanted for their child, there is a grieving process to go through involving denial, guilt, self-doubt and anger. 'What will family and friends think when they find out? Am I to blame in some way? Could it have been prevented?' Or, more selfishly, 'Why are you doing this to us?' Getting used to the idea takes time, and it is often helpful in this situation to talk with other parents of gay youths. The support and advice that can be provided by a group is usually worth enlisting.

Sexual Intercourse—A Health Hazard

You may be able to recall a time when a sexual fantasy was about holding hands. The experts say that petting is dying out, that the leap from a goodnight kiss to intercourse is too quick. This is unfortunate, and sex educators and therapists are trying desperately to revive the notion of 'general pleasuring' as the more appropriate path to sexual happiness. We, as parents, can offer our children important lessons by examples of our affection and loving behaviour.

Meanwhile, with genital sex as all the rage, young people are in danger. There is an ancient saying—'for a little love, you can pay your whole life'. This section looks at why sexual intercourse is such a health hazard.

Teenage Pregnancy

Some teenagers choose to be parents, and although for these young people this represents an enormous challenge, by and large, with support, they do a great job. However, an *unwanted* pregnancy is a tragedy for all concerned whatever the outcome. Usually it is unplanned, although for some girls, a pregnancy is sought (not necessarily at a conscious level) as a way to meet psychological needs. Such girls generally have low self-esteem, are under-achievers, have experienced losses or are in some sort of strife. For them, motherhood is viewed as a means of achieving a sense of self-worth or independence.

In some traditional societies, adolescent pregnancy is an integral part of the culture and occurs under the protection of the family and society. Our society is very different. A frightened teenager with an unexpected pregnancy anticipates parental and social disapproval and will often try to keep it a secret for as long as possible.

What are the main issues and problems?:

- In presenting late for antenatal care, pregnant teenagers put themselves at medical risk; also, the younger and less mature they are, the greater the risks

- Approximately one out of every two teenage pregnancies ends in termination, the physical, psychological and social consequences of which are not always evident in the short term; however, important research conducted by Dr Robert Blum in the United States, has shown that young women seeking an abortion appear to have a more sophisticated ability to project themselves into the future, in comparison to those who go on to have a baby; they are better able to imagine the possible impact that a completed pregnancy might have on themselves and their potential offspring
- When teenage girls choose to continue with their pregnancy, as around half of them do, their lives are permanently affected, usually adversely; these are also the girls, according to the above findings, who feel more controlled by external events and subscribe to far more traditional sexual stereotypes than those who have abortions
- Just over one in ten pregnant girls marry, but teenage marriages are notoriously unstable, with many ending in divorce
- Around four in ten have their babies and raise them as single mothers, a situation fraught with difficulty; the children of adolescent mothers are more likely to be exposed to illness, injury and deprivation and go on to become teenage mothers themselves; some people openly resent the government allowance that single mothers get, viewing it as an unnecessary burden for the taxpayer; contrary to popular belief, girls rarely seek a pregnancy and then keep their baby for financial gain; once there, however, the financial support they receive is minimal so to suggest they should receive less is unthinkable

This is not a happy litany of facts and figures. Pregnant teenage girls face an agonising dilemma and, somehow, must choose for themselves the 'least worst option'. While we now know that there are personality factors involved in the choice they make, it is a decision that is not easily made alone. Understandably, a girl in this situation is going to feel pretty scared about how her mum and dad are going to react when they find out. They're not likely to feel pleased! But, as a rule, it works out better than teenagers expect. Of course a teenager may have an abortion without her parents finding out (a particularly heavy secret to carry). Sometimes there is conflict over what should be done, and pressure may be brought to bear upon her to pursue a course of action contrary to her wishes. Fortunately, most parents tend to rally in a crisis and give all important moral support and guidance. However things turn out and whatever the difficulties along the way, this can make an enormous difference.

The young father, long neglected by researchers and counsellors, is coming under increasing scrutiny. Teenage boys generally do not handle their girlfriends' pregnancy at all well. The relationship often falls apart. They are more likely to be unemployed and have relatively poor prospects for the future, as well as ongoing emotional problems. Somehow or other, they need to be included in the difficult process of sorting things out.

When a girl decides to keep her baby and raise it as a single mother, her parents (unless they have thrown her out and severed ties) often become very involved in its care, even if with some ambivalence at the outset. After all, just when they thought that nappies and broken nights were well behind them, here they are starting anew. However, having to raise a grandchild, more as parents than grandparents, while a frequent bone of contention for the child's young mother, is not without its pleasures and satisfactions for the 'oldies'. Many in this situation tackle it philosophically and with goodwill.

Sometimes, 'premature grandparents' have too high expectations and consider that the adolescent mother, now with a child of her own, should become an instant adult. She can't. She still needs to grow up, and this means going to the occasional disco. Having to turn her back on all the normal things that young people like and do is hardly conducive to her growing up.

Sexually Transmitted Diseases

The incidence of STDs continues to rise worldwide, with young people being largely responsible for this trend. In developed countries, more than two-thirds of all reported cases of gonorrhoea are in people under 25. Chlamydia and trichomonas (see below) are thought to be even more common. The situation has become extremely complex, with more than twenty infectious agents now known to be transmitted sexually.

Owing to inadequate sex education (which also means inadequate communication between parents and kids), teenagers are dangerously ill informed about these diseases. They have some rather strange ideas: nice people don't catch things, you have to sleep around, the best way to get rid of it is to 'give it away'. This means that young people don't take proper precautions (such as using the humble condom, which offers at least some protection), don't recognise symptoms for what they are, and don't readily seek help when they do. Teenagers need to know that disappearance of symptoms does not mean that the disease has gone and need to be convinced that *prevention is better than cure*.

Having, or fearing the possibility of having an STD, is not something that a teenager would readily discuss with parents, unless they are very 'askable' people. Unfortunately, parents themselves are often ill informed and scared about these diseases, a situation that can be remedied by getting hold of the clear and explicit pamphlets put out by the Health Education Council.

Here are a few pertinent facts:

- Gonorrhoea presents itself in many symptomatic guises, such as a very sore throat; usually causes discharge and discomfort in men but may be symptomless in women; homosexual transmission is very common
- There is much concern nowadays about chlamydia; like gonorrhoea, this organism may not cause obvious symptoms, which is why it is being referred to as the 'silent epidemic', but it represents a real risk of infection in the tubes (salpingitis or pelvic inflammatory disease); chlamydia can lead to infertility and other serious medical problems (for example, ectopic pregnancy)
- Genital herpes has also become increasingly common, it is distressing when active and likely to recur
- Some groups of young people (for example, young gays)

are at high risk for STDs, including Hepatitis B and AIDS (which *cannot* be picked up with normal social contact); the message that needs to be stressed is that these serious diseases can be avoided by always using condoms and (for intravenous drug users) never sharing needles and syringes

- Infection with the wart virus (an STD related disease) has been linked to the development of cancer of the cervix occurring in young women; girls who start having sex early and have multiple partners are at particular risk
- 'Thrush' (monilia) causes an itchy white vaginal discharge and is frequently associated with antibiotics, the pill, and the warm, humid environment created by tight jeans and nylon pants
- Trichomonal infection produces an itchy, smelly discharge and is treatable with tablets

The physical dangers of STDs are not the only problem. Emotional traumas associated with contracting these diseases can be serious too. I once diagnosed syphilis in a boy who'd recently had his first and only sexual experience. His partner had been an older woman he'd trusted and he was completely shattered by it.

It's almost enough to put you off sex, especially with anyone you don't know extremely well. With medical concerns about STDs now including the longer term risks of infertility, cancer and AIDS, no one can afford to have a *laissez faire* attitude. While crabs (pubic lice—also sexually transmitted) and thrush can be readily fixed, blocked tubes and AIDS can't. Teenagers need to know, from an early age, what the dangers are and that it pays to be careful.

What Can Parents Do About All This?

Let's bring the subject of teenage sexuality back into the home. Nothing terrible has happened, but there are feelings and vibes everywhere. You are hassling about the usual things—dress, hairstyle, friends and curfews. Most parents don't realise that these are often thinly disguised attempts to control sexual behaviour. An even less direct approach is to say or do nothing that could lead to discussion, conflict or personal revelation about sex. Kids play this game too, knowing their folks need protection from their emerging sexuality.

This is not the way to go. We get ourselves so tied up in knots about it, that there is more stress and anxiety than is necessary. Admittedly, there is a lot of water under the bridge: attitudes arising out of our own upbringing have already been conveyed; our marital (or equivalent) behaviour has already been modelled. But it is still possible to change the state of play. To do so requires a rethink of some enduring misconceptions:

That adolescents are knowledgeable about sex—They may appear so at times, but this is deceiving. Research studies have demonstrated that many teenagers believe: that females have to have an orgasm to conceive; that the 'safe period' (good grief) is in the middle of the cycle; that you don't get pregnant if you have sex standing up etc.

Even if young people get the basic facts straight, what they learn from television is: that being sexy is good; that you have to have sex in different positions; that orgasm is the main goal. No doubt, this falls far short of the attitudes and understanding that most parents would wish them to have.

That if you tell them, they'll want to do it—The fact is, they already want to do it. Far more important questions are, 'how soon' and 'with what degree of forethought, consideration and safety?' The evidence suggests that teenagers 'in the know' are actually more likely to postpone sexual intercourse and be more responsible generally in their sexual behaviour.

That you have to be all knowing—The information explosion and technological advancement in the areas of sexuality and conception are dizzying. Not knowing the answers to complex or even factual questions is no crime. In fact, it might even be an advantage sometimes not to know. Then you could say 'I don't know' or 'My views are not firm on that subject' or 'I'll find out and we can discuss it again'. Young people really appreciate a candid or humble response on these matters.

That you have to be liberal in your attitudes—Who says you have to have a carte blanche attitude to your children's developing sexuality? Is it so terrible to be labelled old fashioned, traditional or boring? A pseudo-liberal posture with undertones of disapproval is worse, and kids can pick it with ease. An open and responsible approach is preferable.

That you have to always be comfortable about sex—For one thing, it's impossible. Talking about it won't always go smoothly, even if you subscribe to the view that questions must be answered frankly and honestly and at the adolescent's level. Anyone can be taken off guard. It's OK to say, 'I feel a bit embarrassed talking about this'.

Then there's the question of what to do if and when you're directly confronted by your teenager's sex life. Suppose your son or daughter wants to bring their girl/boyfriend home for the night or the weekend or on holidays? What do you say then? There's the indignant 'not in my house/separate rooms or nothing' approach (even though you know that they might be sneaking around in the wee hours); or there's the 'turn a blind eye/ open acceptance' approach. A lot depends too on their ages and the nature of the relationship. I once gently threw a nice young man out of my then 15 year old daughter's bedroom. It turned out to be my problem as they were 'just good friends'.

Conclusion

The subject of sexuality for young people is broad. At the very least, it covers identity issues, relationships, communication, moral values, experimentation and societal pressures. Young people need information, opinions and ideas about human sexuality from the adults in their lives. They need opportunities to discuss their sexual feelings and get them into perspective. They need to be encouraged to take things gradually and to enjoy a relationship for the other things it has to offer as well.

When the time comes to experience a sexual relationship, young people need access to counselling and contraceptive advice. Hopefully, at that stage, they will have achieved enough maturity and self-regard to be discriminating, careful and caring. They will be aware of the implications of sexuality for physical and emotional health and take all necessary precautions. Their decisions about who they share their bodies with, however, are their own.

CHAPTER FOUR

Do I Have to Go to School?

Getting an education used to be something you just did, more or less. It was simply the way one spent those particular waking hours, no questions asked. Then, as now, the demands for achievement were not always matched by our thirst for knowledge. Then, as now, the constraints and authority that epitomise school were not always in keeping with our innate desires for freedom and independence. But there, perhaps, the comparison ends.

High schools developed in the expectation of full employment, an expectation, as we now know, never to be fulfilled. This simple but shattering fact has put a gigantic question mark over the whole deal. Teenagers today have particular reason to wonder: education for what? relevance to whom? This hallowed institution, our education system, surrounded by controversy as never before, appears no match for the rapidity with which society is changing.

This chapter looks at the secondary school scene, how parents can help and some of the problems that may arise.

What Are Secondary Schools About?

Like any other system, the education system has its good and bad points, its extremes and its middle ground. Optimists say, in fact, that things are changing, ever so slowly, for the better; that

... education for what?.. relevant to whom?..

there really are discernible moves in the right direction. Some of these are emerging from within the education system itself, while others are occurring in response to outside influences.

School children have the benefit of newer and more effective teaching techniques: there is less of a focus on the rote learning of factual information (although there still seems no better way to learn multiplication tables); experiential learning is in vogue, enabling kids to gain knowledge and understanding through active involvement in the learning process; some schools do justice to the teaching of skills for living (more about this later). Modern education has the capacity, at least, to engage young emotions as well as young intellects.

Schools are also having to adjust to our increasingly multicultural society; the changing aspirations of girls (more of whom now complete secondary school than boys) and a more aware public that would like a greater say in what's happening.

The Pressure's Really On

Meanwhile, for a lot of kids, school is not all that great a place. It should be a responsive and caring place, more even than a centre of learning and stimulation—a place that draws young people to its heart and serves their needs. In reality, many are merely 'stuck' there, victims to pressures beyond their control. Even teachers are recognising that secondary school can be a bruising experience for young people, an allegation that deserves our serious attention.

The **outside pressures** are to do with being at school and with staying there as long as possible. The latter pressures come frcm parents, from schools and, increasingly, from governments. As jobs for young people are becoming fewer and further between, anxieties are being transmitted to school children down through the years, even to primary school. These days, a little kid who fails at blocks is being watched very closely as a future could be in jeopardy. (On the other hand, Woody Allen claims he 'failed at milk' and look how well he's done!)

There are **inside pressures** too, mostly to do with conforming and achieving. What's wrong with pressure to conform? Isn't this what society demands of us all, with its precise rules and bureaucratic systems? However, if school is about getting on with the job (one that is devised and perpetrated entirely by adults, as it happens) in an atmosphere of mindless obedience, lots of kids are in hot water.

Of course, persistently wearing your tie crooked is a different brand of recalcitrance, perhaps, to always turning up late and, one would imagine, less outrageous than punching up smaller kids. But even in matters of dress and etiquette, in some schools, transgressions can get you into very serious strife indeed.

How many kids involved in the normal questioning of authority have heard the challenge, 'And what makes you think you're special, Buster?' Sadly, many schools seem unable or unwilling to view emerging individuality as a positive attribute. If education is designed to shape rather than to encourage growth in young people, we may indeed be involved in 'training for docility'.

What's wrong with pressure to achieve? Surely that's not altogether a bad thing either? Surely everyone wants kids to do as well as possible?

It depends—Pressure to achieve academically is what this is usually about, and it's certainly not going to suit everyone. Secondary school students cope with academic pressure in several ways:

There Are Those Who Compete and Win—Teenagers who do well in the academic arena bring pride to their parents, kudos to the school and seem pointed towards a bright and successful future. But this is not always without cost:

- Some 'brainy' kids are ostracised by their peers or become social isolates by choice, which is not the best way to become a functional and well rounded person
- Success may be achieved at the expense of emotional or physical health; many high achieving students are on legal medications, such as analgesics or tranquillizers, for headaches or other stress related symptoms

Amongst the most stressed (and unwell) high achievers I have seen professionally, are those from notoriously high pressure schools, where kids without supreme potential are not allowed in to start with—mustn't mess up the school average. Knowing that pupils who don't make the grade are likely to be gently 'encouraged to leave', and that their parents know this too, is a heavy burden to carry.

There Are Those Who Compete and Lose—Some kids do less well than they would wish, or than others would wish, despite trying hard. Studies have shown that concerns about school, including exam results, are rated highly by teenagers. Struggling on without success provides an assault to self-esteem and feelings of guilt at not living up to personal, family or teacher expectations.

As one young struggler put it, 'If I didn't feel that everyone was on my back so much, I think I'd probably do better'. Young people who constantly fall short of expectations are at risk of depression—a chastening thought. There is value in parents talking to the teenager and teachers with a view to agreeing on realistic expectations. It makes a big difference.

There Are Those Who Refuse to Compete at All—For non-academic pupils, the main problem is lack of gratification. The system doesn't meet their needs, they become bored and disruptive and usually opt out early. Actually, some opt out and physically leave, others opt out and stay put, being present only in body. Of those who leave, a lucky few will find a job, but most, with nothing to go to, will merely join the ranks of the restless unemployed. Some school drop-outs, in cahoots with kindred spirits, will get up to no good (which is unfortunate, perhaps, for public telephones and train seats).

Secondary School Is a Family Affair

Despite all this, parents don't need to be told that secondary school is important. In the classroom and in the playground, important life dramas are being played out and destinies are being determined. We may be totally confused as to what our kids are supposed to be learning (although it is possible to find out). We may share their uncertainty as to how pertinent it all is to what lies ahead for them. We may even be unaware of whether or not they are receiving the best education available.

It is our duty and responsibility as parents, however, to encourage and support young people in their efforts to learn what there is to learn, to cope with school and to make the best of it. Being interested in what is going on and getting involved when the opportunity is there, cannot be underestimated.

First Things First

Anticipation of secondary school really hits home in the final year at primary school. Some kids are starting to physically develop at this time and become more independent. Others seem too little, too immature for what is facing them. But if they're the right age, and they've made the grade, off they go to join the 'big guys'. The question is, 'Which secondary school?'

For some families, things just fall into place. Maybe there's only one option, or the decision was made long ago. Some parents book their kids into private schools of their choice at birth—the so called 'birthday booking'. In other situations, however, there are choices to make, pros and cons to consider and conflicts to resolve. Some kids will want to go where their friends go, and cannot see much beyond that. (It's a valid case, particularly if they're anxious about the whole deal.) Parents, on the other hand, are thinking ahead and wondering what's for the best. Their own aspirations and values come into the picture, making it an emotive subject.

A high proportion of secondary school students is receiving a private education, and there appears to be a community trend in this direction. In making this choice however, parents are motivated by a number of issues:

- A desire to find a school that more or less reflects the family's values (and sometimes this can include an element of snobbery)
- A desire to find a school that will suit the particular needs of the child (for example, a sensitive kid will usually be more comfortable in a smaller school)
- A belief that higher educational standards will be available (although recent studies show that degree success rates are higher

for students from state school backgrounds)

- An interest in discipline, usually of the traditional, 'character building' sort

As for single sex versus mixed sex schools, the debate rages on. Girls do better academically in single sex secondary schools (hence the joke about having to choose between a co-educational school and an educational one). But when boys' and girls' schools have amalgamated, achievement levels in maths and English have not greatly suffered. Also, there appears to be no guarantee that any academic advantage will carry over into university or polytechnic education.

Ten years of classroom research show that teachers address most of their teaching to boys (as much as 80 per cent), even when they think they're not. They do this, apparently, because boys are noisier, present more behavioural problems and demand more attention than girls. Some people believe, probably correctly, that it's mostly due to sexism. Whatever the reasons, it's not fair, and it's understandable that parents are concerned about it.

There is, however, a powerful argument in favour of mixed sex schools, and it relates to psychological and social factors. These have been much less studied, but teenagers have a less stereotyped image of the opposite sex, and learn to relate more comfortably as friends in the co-ed situation. For both boys and girls, self-esteem is better too.

An Important Transition

Moving on to secondary school is a major milestone for children, one that often stirs mixed feelings of excitement and apprehension. Primary school has provided a highly structured, predictable and relatively low pressure environment. Kids know that secondary school is different, that it involves new subjects, assorted teachers (some of whom are sure to be awful) and class to class moves. There are also more people to cope with and, most importantly, a sudden change of status—you become the youngest again!

Anxieties are short lived, however, decreasing usually within the first few days. After 3 weeks, it is estimated that nine out of ten first year pupils are feeling comfortably settled in. Some schools have 'peer support schemes' in which older pupils take an interest in the newcomers, show them the ropes and lend a helping hand. This seems to work well and everyone involved feels good.

$$\mathbf{x} = \frac{-\mathbf{b} \pm \sqrt{\mathbf{b}^2 - 4\mathbf{ac}}}{2\mathbf{a}}$$

If an adolescent seems uptight about something, it means a lot when a parent quietly takes note of it—'I bet you're feeling a bit anxious about school', for example. It's a question of empathy. You can also listen to a tirade about dastardly injustice in the classroom or mayhem in the school playground, and feel well within your element. This is a manageable parental role. But when it comes to helping with homework, good intentions may not be enough!

How can you possibly help if you've never put a finger to a microcomputer? You might even know how to get the right answer to a maths problem (your way!), but they do things differently now.

Depending on the year and the school, homework is really piled on. Multiple assignments and self-directed study are hallmarks of modern secondary education and are, no doubt, all for the better. But there's so little time for fun, to just muck around. For secondary school students, out of school hours (certainly on weekdays) are regimented and serious—there's no other way to cope with the load.

I have a friend who tells me about the regular maths coaching he gives his son. I listen in awe. Personally, it troubles me that my own kids will remember me as an utterly inept homework helper. Their subjects seem too complicated for mere parental mortals. My 14 year old son wanted ideas for a cover design for Harper Lee's classic novel, *To Kill a Mocking Bird*. 'Not a bloody chicken with an arrow through it', he cautioned. He'd read my mind.

Fortunately, there are ways for parents to help, without losing face:

- Show an interest, from time to time, in your teenager's subjects; the options here are to do a little research, by glancing through set texts and novels, or simply make encouraging noises (even if you haven't got a clue what the subject is about)
- Try not to nag about homework; it's more effective, as a rule, to exhibit a quiet acceptance that homework is important—the school will let you know if there are problems
- Encourage good study methods, such as the making of regular summaries in each subject
- If possible, create a calm and studious atmosphere while homework is underway (family squabbles can be scheduled for another time maybe?)
- Be strong—limit weekday television; it's a deadly enemy of homework

Exams Take Their Toll

Exams serve their purpose, but are not always beneficial to one's mental health. I have seen a 17 year old girl who became psychotic during the first of her 'A' level exams. More final year students are turning up with emotional problems than ever before. Near exam time, anxious teenagers consult their doctors with headaches, sore elbows and wrists and all sorts of other stress related symptoms.

On the other hand, I know of one set of parents who had no idea their daughter was doing an important exam, until the very morning it was on! Between total nonchalance and gut-churning panic, however, there's a good deal of concern and worry. For the majority, exam tension is unavoidable. Even now, seeing blossom gives me 'butterflies' in the stomach (their association with summertime exams etched for ever in my brain).

What can parents do to help? The general advice given above still applies, only more so. Apart from walking on eggs and discouraging visitors, parents can further oblige with a predictable home routine, meals that are served hot and exactly on time, and a flexible approach to household chores (the harried student's participation in them, that is). This is called 'understanding'. Of course, a decent place to work and a utopian homelife are not adequate in themselves. Teenagers also need 'exam preparation skills', something, hopefully, the school can provide.

The School Report

The school report, another interesting phenomenon, is designed to indicate, directly to parents, how a pupil is getting along. Much time and effort usually go into its preparation. With its interesting array of marks, symbols, averages, comments and exhortations, it is meant to provide a clear blueprint of the current state of affairs. The comments are particularly important, although sometimes, you have to read between the lines.

In his third year first term report, a teenage boy received the following 'compliments': in Maths, he was 'polite and co-operative'; in Home Science (which he topped), 'a zealous worker with an excellent attitude'; in English, 'talkative and inattentive'; in History, 'thoughtful and positive in discussion'. In Geography, however, 'He must learn that the teacher's decision is final. It is *not* his place to oppose the teacher'. School reports tell you something about the teacher too.

Often parents pay too much attention to the mark, and too little to the effort, a mistake to be avoided at all costs. Some schools send instructions home on how to deal with the report, and encourage parents to respond sensitively. After all, it is not the intention to create unnecessary tension and unhappiness. The main don'ts are as follows:

- Don't talk with other parents about the results (not too specifically, anyway)
- Don't openly compare the reports of siblings
- Don't refer back and openly compare with earlier reports—it's now that counts (although a steady decline could certainly be an indicator of stress)
- Don't offer bribes for future improvement—there are better incentives than a trip to Disneyland; your personal

modelling of high standards and your respect and interest in their progress should pay dividends in themselves

- Don't panic, hit the roof and pile on more counter-productive pressure (expectations might be too great already)

Teachers are People Too

The question, 'What is a good teacher?' is often debated. There is no single, universally accepted answer. Is it someone who is knowledgeable in the subject area and can put it across in a stimulating manner? Is it someone who cracks jokes from time to time and shows a human face? Probably all this and more. Adolescents need room to move as individuals and greatly value a teacher who provides it. They also need positive reinforcement, as everybody does, and someone they can trust.

A good teacher is long remembered, an inspiration for life. An English teacher I know encourages her secondary school pupils to communicate with her through a journal. This is purely voluntary. Kids can write to her about anything they wish, knowing they will receive back a caring comment, a simple word of encouragement or advice. They would probably describe her as a 'good teacher'.

Some parents seem intimidated by teachers, whether they're good, bad or indifferent, and avoid them at all costs. Parent and teacher nights come and go and they stay at home. For those who do go, however, suitably armed with teenage gossip, it can be an extremely informative and worthwhile experience.

There are other gains as well. Knowing who you are, teachers say, makes a difference to their attitude to the pupil, who then becomes more than just a face in the crowd. The triangular relationship between the school, the child and the parent is an extremely important one, and teachers are certain that their efforts are more potent when parents are aware, encouraging and involved in what's happening. As a result, you too can get things into better perspective and your teenager, who'll be aware that you've taken the trouble, cannot help but feel good.

School Problems

Actually, secondary school teachers don't have an easy time. They need holidays (which some people seem to resent) to save their sanity. As well as having responsibility for as many as seven separate classes, material to prepare daily, exams to mark and standards to maintain, teachers are also expected to identify and help kids with problems.

School problems are common, with possibly as many as three in ten students having academic or behavioural difficulties. The major concerns are about poor performance, poor attendance and poor behaviour. Here is some information about these problems:

Poor Performance

The essence of underachievement is expectation. Someone thinks the student can do better, and is usually right. The reasons may not be deep: bright kids may become bored and stop trying; some are turned off by excessive pressure or an 'irrevelant' curriculum (a feeling that future employment prospects are bleak anyway, and that 'learning this stuff' won't help); others simply have different priorities and 'march to the beat of a different drum'. Poor or deteriorating grades, however, can also mean emotional problems or specific learning difficulties.

Emotional problems (the most common cause of all school problems), should be suspected in the presence of anxiety, sadness or anger related to events in a young person's life. Worry and stress short circuit energy away from the task of learning, which makes falling marks a particularly sensitive indicator that something is amiss. It may be problems at home, although teasing and other hassles at school, either by peers or teachers, can really get kids down too.

Specific learning difficulties should be suspected when there are particular problems with spelling, reading and mathematics; left-right confusion or a sort of 'absent minded professor' approach to information. This can also show up in IQ tests which, while discredited for general usage, have a characteristic pattern where specific learning difficulties are concerned. Learning difficulties are more common than we realise and the earlier they are picked up the better. Behaviour problems, related mostly to frustration, are often the clue and are extremely common in boys. (The frustration that girls experience is generally not quite as obvious and, for this reason it is thought that their learning difficulties may be underidentified.) Some of these kids are reluctant to go to school or may develop some other form of anxiety.

The assessment of specific learning difficulties is complex, with many different factors needing to be taken into account. It could include, for example: a thorough medical/neurological examination, a battery of psychological tests, a psychiatric assessment, a language evaluation, and an educational diagnosis. It is helpful to have someone you trust such as your family doctor or one of the specialists co-ordinating the whole procedure. There is also a bewildering array of interventions, but no known cure. Remember, no individual expert necessarily has the answer. Don't be afraid to ask questions and don't get discouraged.

Another reason for poor performance may rest with the quality of the teaching. Teenagers may do badly in subjects taught by teachers they don't like (usually because they're boring, ill prepared, sarcastic or punitive). It's worth checking out.

Poor Attendance

Going to school can sometimes be a real drag, but as already discussed, it's not simply a matter of choice. For better or worse, secondary education has been compulsory in the UK, for children under 16, since the 1950s. There was a time when not showing up would soon see the authorities knocking on your door. Recently, they've become too busy with other things (mostly abuse and neglect cases) to do much about it, which really leaves parents in a quandary.

Teenagers won't turn up at school for various reasons. They may be seriously ill or disabled, often needing time out to visit doctors or physios or to be in hospital. Parents may actually encourage them to stay at home to help out with domestic chores or child care. This is not uncommon in families where education is not greatly valued. Then there are young people who consciously 'skive' off school in order to do something more enjoyable, such as playing in the park, seeing a movie or refining their electronic skills at pinball parlours. While some kids play truant just for the hell of it (hoping, of course, that no one will find out), sometimes they become involved in other problem behaviour such as stealing, vandalism and drug abuse. Then it is obviously a more serious problem.

Sometimes, kids don't go to school for psychological reasons. In the condition called 'school refusal' (or school phobia), a child or adolescent may fear or be reluctant to attend school, despite a desire to do so. Obviously, this is very different to truancy and much less fun. When a kid consistently says, 'I've got a headache', only on school mornings, something's going on. It may appear that a stressful situation or event at school is responsible, but in most cases, the underlying problem is getting out of the front door and leaving home.

Quite a lot is known about school refusing children and their families. There is often anxiety about losing a parent (usually the mother) and staying at home is a way to keep track of things. Many of these kids (about half) are depressed, timid individuals who are afraid of new experiences. Of course, the involved parent may also be holding onto the child. Often family therapy or some other sort of counselling can help the young person gain the courage to move towards independence, and help the family relinquish control.

Poor Behaviour

'Are teachers there to teach you?', asked a girl in her final year at primary school, 'or are they there to get you in trouble?' This plaintive question raises an important point: what is 'poor behaviour'? Lack of attentiveness? Some kids explain that it is very difficult for them to be 'bright eyed and bushy tailed' at 8.30 in the morning. Some teenagers, it seems, are just not 'morning people'.

A pattern of aggressive or oppositional behaviour, on the other hand, is a worrying sign, especially when accompanied by school failure. Teenagers who resist the usual limit setting and consistently infringe the rights of others are in a special category. For teachers, such kids are extremely taxing, often intimidating and ultimately soul destroying.

Mostly though, the shoe is on the other foot. Teachers have the upper hand and may not always use it with compassion. I vividly remember one of my teachers (perhaps better described as a sadist) who set a spelling test every Monday morning, and caned anyone who got less than a perfect score. We would line up around the walls (sometimes the entire class) and one by one, present an outstretched hand. On one occasion, he gave one 'cut' for each mistake.

This style of corporal punishment is no longer acceptable, but has been part of a spectrum of measures designed to control kids. Teachers and schools vary greatly in their handling of discipline problems. Other techniques include: a sympathetic exploration of the underlying reasons for the behaviour, a symbolic gesture such as loss of privileges, suspension from classes (the ignominy of working alone), physical detention after school hours—with or without the writing out of lines, the use of peer discipline (for example, having to clean a prefect's shoes), or explusion from school—usually a drastic last resort.

To what extent the more serious measures are deserved, necessary or helpful is difficult to say. Some kids seem too readily labelled as bad, when there are clearly other factors at work. Some kids who play up are those who cannot see the relevance in what they're doing, lose respect for educational values and become disenchanted with the authority of teachers.

There's another worrying thought. The people who do best in life are those who have self-confidence and feel good about themselves. These attributes are less likely to develop if the measures used to control students' behaviour involve fear, stress, uncertainty, confusion and failure. Enlightened schools know this and act accordingly.

Treatment of School Problems

Not all kids with school problems have specific learning difficulties or require disciplinary measures. As teachers well know, a class is made up of differing individuals with a wide range of abilities and personalities. In a given situation, it will be necessary to look closely at the young person causing concern in order to work out what is best.

There may be a need for tutoring or a change of school in order to get a fresh start. If children are unwell they will need treatment. If this is a stress related disorder or there are other emotional problems involved, then professional counselling may be needed. In most situations, the school will be able to point parents in the right direction.

What About Skills for Living?

From time to time, we hear that all too familiar call to 'get back to the basics'. This sounds reasonable enough as it's a tough and competitive world out there. But life is somewhat more complex than it once was, and the teaching of *skills for living* appears to be in dangerously short supply.

Almost 30 years ago, the wonderful American psychologist-cum-entertainer, Dr Murray Banks, was pointedly asking, 'How many schools teach kids how to deal with worry, or how to get a good discount?' Not many! Young people frequently finish their schooling not knowing how to balance an account, or not knowing even how their body works. While a businessman might be aghast that so few people understand the workings of the economy (and blame the education system), the latter is of greater concern to me.

A colleague and I conducted a class on adolescent health for fifth years at a public girls' secondary school. This was part of their monthly 'Personal Development' programme. (At least they had one!) Approximately eighty, 16 year old girls, eyes alight with anticipation, trouped into a large hall where we awaited them. We got them to determine the agenda, which included: obesity, insecurity about weight and anorexia nervosa (about 80 per cent of them were on diets), pregnancy, abortion and STDs, drugs, hepatitis and (last but not least) acne.

Quite a lot to tackle in a single, 50 minute class. While teenagers seem very keen to discuss these (and other) matters, there are few opportunities to do so. Community ambivalence about just how much schools take on is clearly one of the problems. For parents, it is partly a question of trust, because teachers are viewed as powerful, and competing, influences. We want to be sure that we approve of the ideas, attitudes and values that they are conveying to our children.

Fair enough, but when asked, the majority of parents and pupils agree that sex education should be given in schools. An influential minority remains adamantly opposed to it, and brings enormous pressure to bear on school principals and the education system not to include such subjects in the curriculum.

Where sex education is offered, however, parents and pupils usually have a say. The direct and candid approach taken by the headmaster of one secondary school gained my admiration. In a letter to parents of first year students (12 and 13 years olds), he stated the following:

> We intend to teach sex education in secondary school. This will be part of the Personal Development Course and will continue through the secondary school years. The subject matter dealt with will be suitable to the ages of the students. This may, we hope, allow the pupils to grow up with a full and mature attitude to this important part of our lives.

Actually, health education is happening in schools, whether or not there is any sort of systematic approach to it. Like parents, teachers are models for the young, and kids have their antennae out at all times. So much is imbibed from the climate and attitudes in the school. What's the point of teaching good nutrition in the classroom, for example, and having junk food in the tuck-shop?

What about skills for living? The argument in favour is as follows: we live in stressful and uncertain times, secondary schools have an enormous captive audience of young people and, in order to become functional and competent human beings, they must learn to command their personal resources (intellectual, emotional and physical). By all means teach kids the basics and teach them how to learn. But if our education system abdicates responsibility for these other issues, we're all in big trouble.

Conclusion

Did it ever occur to you that parents get a double dose of schooling? Firstly there's your own, then there's your children's. If your school days were the very best days of your life (well, it's possible) and your kids are doing OK, this is fine, no big deal. If not, it can seem like an endless and exhausting saga.

In either case, being positive about your teenager's school and expressing your personal interest in what is happening now is extremely important. Again, the pupil, the teacher and the parent make up the educational triangle, and the success of the whole exercise depends on each of the three components being actively and effectively involved. Not only do kids spend a great deal of their young lives in school, but their education is their stepping stone to the future.

FAMILY LIFE

SIGH!

CHAPTER FIVE

Middlescence

Middle age has an impact on teenagers. Sooner or later, Mum and Dad will go through it, nothing surer, because Nature has arranged things rather strangely. While kids are going through adolescence, parents are going through 'middlescence'. Have you ever thought that you too, are in transition?

Adults have their own special needs and problems that young people are often unable to recognise and unlikely to understand. (To them, anyone over about 26 seems ancient anyway!) Inevitable differences in circumstance and attitude give rise to all sorts of conflicts and misunderstandings. There exists what we might call an 'empathy gap'.

What Does It Mean to Be Grown Up?

If I thoroughly understood human nature it might be possible to give a confident answer to this question. Some people do seem pretty grown up, in the sense that they say and do the types of things one expects of adults: you know, express opinions on current affairs; hold down a job; go to meetings and help out at the school tuckshop. But how they feel inside generally remains hidden.

One thing is certain, maturity does not descend upon you like a gown of honour around your eighteenth birthday. There is a lot more personal sorting out to do, and it literally might take forever. At some point, however (probably during the thirties), you sense a subtle change in self-concept. You gradually become aware of being more confident in your own beliefs and actions and less concerned with the expectations and demands of others (the boss excluded, of course). The world looks real because you are able to see it as it is and to accept the good and bad as part of life. People who are always complaining don't seem to have come to grips with this.

When Is Middle Age?

This is a touchy business. Can you count on the fingers of more than one hand, people who admit to it willingly? A friend of mine, who looks about 50, vehemently denied that he was middle aged. 'Not even close', he stated bravely, 'I will be suddenly old one day, when it suits me!' Some people feel young inside and that's the way they stay.

Attitudes to ageing have clearly changed. Nowadays, depending on your vantage point of course, even 60 can seem positively young. One reason for this is that there are more really old people around—a tribute to the wonders of modern medicine and national health service. It gives middle aged folk something to be optimistic about.

So, when is it? An age range of 35 to 50 has been suggested for middlescence. Don't be alarmed, this has something going for it. Firstly, it starts exactly half way through our allotted three score and ten, and secondly, this is the period during which one's children are most likely to become adolescents (which is when you'll probably start to feel middle aged anyway).

When Are You a Middlescent?

There can be much satisfaction in reaching middle age, resting on your laurels a little (unless you're an incurable workaholic) and accepting things as they are. But descriptions of middle age for some reason, rarely emphasise the positive. The following is a check list of generally accepted symptoms:

- A growing preoccupation with one's body, its changing shape and assorted discomforts

- A less starry eyed view of male-female relationships (so this is the way it is)
- A sometimes painful evaluation of one's life goals, objectives and achievements (has it all been worth the effort?); if you knew then what you know now, would you have wasted so much time?
- A feeling of being sandwiched between two generations (and not particularly appreciated by either)
- An acceptance of oneself as an older rather than a younger person (some people are born to it); it's harder to find clothes that are just right, not too young and not too old
- A tendency to think more in terms of how much time is left, than of what has gone before; you stop looking forward to birthdays

The Urge for Change

Just when society wants stability from its adult members, the urge for change is strongest. Middle age demands a fresh outlook on life, and the struggles involved in this are complicated and taxing. Some people weather it with relative ease, while others experience a major mid-life crisis that can blow families apart. However, few are immune from the emotional upheavals involved. A close friend of mine who is approaching 40 suddenly and unexpectedly yearns for the past. 'I want to be back in 1974', he pines, 'when my life was free and easy'.

A comparison of the two sorts of 'menopause' should help clarify what's going on:

The so called **male menopause**, albeit a ridiculous phrase, is an important concept. There is nothing hormonal about it at all, but somewhere between the late thirties and mid to late forties, many men become 'ratty' (possibly two-thirds or more). At the very gateway to middle age they fall apart; just when everything in life seems to be going well, they experience an illogical and consuming need for change, a vague and constant sense of frustration and failure.

A previously reasonable man may become irritable and short

tempered, hypochondriacal and complaining, listless and morose. On the other hand, he may become frenetically busy, drink too much (coffee, tea, alcohol, anything) and turn into a restless, nocturnal prowler. More seriously, he may start dressing young and trendy, stay out late 'keeping up with the boys' or going out with young floozies (in search of sexual adventure to bolster up his flagging ego). Of course, what he most wants and needs is understanding and care, something he feels he's unlikely to find at home.

The **female menopause**, as everybody knows, is a totally hormonal phenomenon, usually occurring after the age of 50 and having both physical and emotional manifestations (the former of which can at least be medically controlled). But women too, from a younger age, can experience feelings of uselessness and redundancy that are not hormonal. They have lots of self-doubts, aided and abetted by society's double standard about ageing, which says it's OK for men but not for women.

Research clearly indicates that women who have developed interests outside the home (work related or other) rather than just staying home and devoting themselves to the family, suffer less 'suburban neurosis' and generally fare better psychologically in middle age than those who don't. Of course, few would not welcome hearing, from time to time, that they still look attractive.

For either sex, the essence of the midlife crisis is grieving the loss of the possible. It requires you to graciously give up the idea that you will ever become a sex goddess, achieve fame and fortune as a trapeze artist or single handedly change the world.

Differences in Common

Adolescence has been described as 'a brief period of optimism separating a period of ignorance from a more enduring period of terminal cynicism.' If that's what the generation gap is about, we had better give up now.

Large or small, people are people, and beyond the basics—food, clothing and shelter—we all crave and need certain things. We want to be understood and appreciated, cared for and loved, and acknowledged for our efforts and achievements. We seek variety, enjoyment and meaning in our lives. In as many ways as parents and teenagers are different, therefore, they are also alike. Having some insights into the various concerns that adolescents and middlescents somehow share, can help a lot when the going gets tough.

Changing Bodies

They say middle age has arrived when someone tells you to pull in your stomach, and you already have! Instead of combing your hair, you start 'arranging' it. One does tend to notice, on the other hand, that teenagers are blessed with young, nubile bodies, all supple and firm. Any mother who's shared a bathroom with a 15 year old daughter getting ready for a date, will recognise the feelings involved. There's a fine line sometimes, between admiration and resentment.

A couple of decades has to make some difference to a body, and the fact that most of the changes provide little cause for celebration, is really nobody's fault. Of course, kids are not necessarily revelling in their bodily changes either; teenage concerns about puberty are many and varied. To a 40 year old parent who's starting to discover 'worn bearings and large patches of rust', however, this might not rate too highly at all.

Not Tonight, I'm Too Tired

Seen through adult eyes, teenagers appear to have a powerful sexuality. Those in the throes of puberty in particular, tend to find practically everything erotic. This is not always troubling, but grownups can respond in a number of different ways:

- By feeling uncomfortable and anxious, which can lead to controlling or rejecting behaviour; for example, fathers who feel uncomfortable by the emerging sexuality of their daughters (even though they may not be aware of this at a conscious level) may behave distantly, or exert heavy authority concerning, say, modest dress and behaviour
- By feeling aroused by teenagers which is not all that unusual in itself (although acting on these feelings can be dangerous for both parties)
- By feeling envious, because they seem to be having all the fun (going to parties and having the stamina to stay up late)
- By feeling disappointed and resentful, because you're not having any fun at all (stuck at home watching television, possibly because they've got the car!)

Middle age can be tough from a sexual point of view. It is a time of extremes. The stereotype of inevitable sexual decline is not entirely wrong. Work pressures, financial worries or any of the myriad of other concerns of everyday life, simply make sex a low priority. Performance can suffer (and hormone injections are definitely not the answer). The other side of the coin is a sudden resurgence of erotic fantasies and sexual energy. It's either feast or famine.

One of the problems for middle aged couples is a discrepancy in sexual interest. While it obviously matters, this is not entirely about how much sex they are having (or more likely, not having). The popular press has often pushed the idea of some ephemeral norm (such as once a week) and this too creates guilt and resentment, especially in the partner who believes it. But there are other dangers too. As your years of attractiveness become finite, you may start to question whether you want to spend them all with your traditional partner (who may be wondering the same). Those who successfully weather these unavoidable changes can consider themselves extremely fortunate.

Taking Stock

For most people, the middle years are not too bad, for some, never better. By dint of hard work or good fortune, they will have achieved as much authority and standing as they are destined to achieve. Certainly, it is an appropriate time to take stock, and, if one is spared the more drastic forms of agonising restlessness described above, this is not so terrible. It can rarely be avoided altogether, because time has brought you to a crossroads. But now, with the struggles and frenzy of earlier years behind you, it should be possible to enter more tranquil waters and enjoy the fruits of accomplishment and security.

Teenagers, 'with tomorrow in their eyes', cannot relate easily to their parents' situation. They are caught up in school pressures and vocational anxieties. To them, the relative success and comfort that age apparently brings, seem light years away. Parents are generally well imbued with the good old work ethic too, which can make it even more difficult for them to empathise with modern day dilemmas facing the young, especially unemployment. These particular differences in status and circumstance are not easily bridged.

Did Someone Say 'Independence'?

It's a nice idea, independence, but probably a bit of a myth. Teenagers certainly want it, passionately, and in the process of their struggling for it, parents can go quietly crazy. It's a tug of war about freedom, control and responsibility, all the things that kids seem to think grownups have. Meanwhile, parents may be discovering that they have a little more responsibility than they need. Middle aged people largely run the country, manage the businesses, and carry the various burdens related to community life. It doesn't always feel great.

If you're lucky, of course, your parents are still alive, self-supporting and 'with it'. Even so, there is often a distinct feeling in the middle years of being squeezed from both sides. So much for independence! Whatever one's age, our parents continue to exert a powerful influence over us. We may not always understand it, but chances are we do take it seriously.

My wife relates the following story which has now entered our family folklore. It concerns a dreadful, sleepless night in which she had to contend with: a fractious, feeding baby on one side, a slightly older child (who was having nightmares) on the other side, and a disgruntled and complaining husband next to her. 'Can't you settle those kids?', I'm alleged to have said, 'I've got a really busy day tomorrow'. Some time later, my wife was relating this sad tale to my mother who, instinctively no doubt, exclaimed, 'Oh dear, poor David'!

Everybody has unresolved issues related to their parents which can range from minor irritations about their attitudes and behaviour, to deep seated emotional pain persisting from childhood. Coming to terms with these feelings is an important task of adulthood. Sometimes, as Harold H. Bloomfield has pointed out, what you have to deal with is the 'internal conflict between you and the parents you carry inside your head'. While your children won't understand this now, they will later.

I've never forgotten the gist of a Woody Allen one liner from the film, *Manhattan*: 'Apart from sex and my mother', he said, 'I think I've got things pretty well sorted out'. A reasonable comment on middle age, perhaps?

What Does It All Mean?

Young people and their middlescent parents also have in common a search for meaning to life. Both are asking: 'What is it all about?' 'Where am I headed?' Middle aged people, of course, are not doing this for the first time, but they are offered a golden opportunity. This new bout of self-questioning is a way to resolve certain left over bits of adolescence that didn't get sorted out before. There is time also to reflect, even to get in touch with one's spiritual self. This can be an uncomfortable and unsettling process, and your canny kids will know how to prod it along. But chances are, you'll come through it a better person (and possibly a little more mature.)

In a sense too, the rapid social change of the past 20 years or so has brought the two generations closer together. For example, confusion about what's going on, the necessity to become computer literate, and concerns about the state of the world and dangers to mankind are all shared. Kids may get churned up about what they view as a 'tarnished legacy', but most adults aren't too happy about it either.

The Impossible Dream

So, there we have it. Nature, society and the passage of time set us up. For young people, the world is an oyster and they are the future. For middlescent parents, the realisation is dawning that certain goals and ambitions will never be achieved. They are becoming aware that there is a limit to the length and quality of their lives, and they're not necessarily going to take it lying down.

Teenagers don't have a clear picture of this. How could they? Nobody explains it to them. But they know something's going on and it can be extremely puzzling. Consider some of the stranger things that some parents are doing in their middle years:

- To be *successful*, they're spending all their time at work or sitting on committees (usually with people they can't stand)

- To be *healthy*, they're getting heavily into vitamins and health food (even if they don't feel better, it's nice to be helping a struggling growth industry)
- To be *fit*, they're jogging up and down village, town or inner city streets (deeply inhaling toxic fumes and risking injury or death in the unfeeling traffic)
- To be *in touch* with their inner selves, they're embracing special therapies (for the scientifically inclined—biofeedback; for those who want to start all over again—primal therapy; for those who prefer a subtle blend of social and spiritual activities—group yoga)
- To be *calm*, and when all else fails, they're getting into alcohol or tranquillizers (which can get very out of hand!)

The Stiff Upper Lip

What about the brave souls who merely grin and bear it? Aren't grownups supposed to be rational and responsible at all times? No matter what's happening in their lives, aren't they expected to be strong, to cope, to have no problems, confusions or self-doubts? If this is what you think, read on, fast.

Middle aged parents are notoriously reluctant to discuss their personal difficulties. They believe that adults should be able to solve their own problems. This stoic attitude not only doubles the burden, but it isn't too good for the kids either. It's really hard to relate to a stiff upper lip!

Teenagers need parents who are comfortable with themselves, who accept the ups and downs of life and who know what to do when life becomes really stressful and demanding. One of the most important goals for middle aged parents is to reduce the empathy gap, to keep the lines of communication open so that mutual understanding can grow. This requires, first of all, that you give up being a closed book, and secondly, that you are able to put yourself in their shoes (to some extent, at least).

So Open Up a Little

Children and adolescents love parents to talk about themselves. Have you ever noticed that? 'Tell us again, Dad. What else did you do when you were a child?'

There is nothing quite so humanising as self-revelation. This is different from wearing your heart on your sleeve. I am talking about a judicious sharing of one's thoughts, feelings and experiences; from funny little things that happen at work, to major, embarrassing gaffs. After all, this is who you are. Why keep it to yourself?

An ability to do this makes it more likely too that you will avail yourself of support when you need it. Given its amazing health promoting qualities, support is one of our most underrated therapies. It consists of anyone or anything that makes a person feel better, function better or be more optimistic. Often it's a matter of gaining information that gives one a sense of being more in control. The most powerful sources of support open to an individual are one's intimate relationships with family or friends (teenage children included).

Sometimes, of course, problems are such that more is required. What you need then is a good 'therapist', someone who's not only competent, but also empathic, warm, and seems genuinely interested in you. There are such people around.

Take a Nostalgic Trip

L. P. Hartley said in *The Go Between*, 'The past is a foreign country, they do things differently there'. But memory is a wonderful thing, for it enables you to go there. One important way of closing the empathy gap is to picture yourself as a teenager. What did you look like and what caused you embarrassment? Do you remember your first heavy date or your first sexual experience (as if anyone doesn't!). What was it like? Who was your best friend and what did you do together? What was going on around you? What was most likely to cause arguments with your parents and what were the things they did that bugged you the most? What didn't you tell them? How did you get along at school and who was the teacher you hated most? What was very important to you at the time and what were your dreams for the future?

This is terrific fun to do in a group, particularly if you all went through it in the same decade. Be prepared for a lot of laughter, but the memories might be bitter sweet (or even a touch painful.) That is, after all, what adolescence is like.

Conclusion

Bad jokes about middle age are pretty common, but for many men and women, turning 40 is no laughing matter. Some people buckle under and thereafter devote all their waning energies to accelerating downwards. Others cope well, hold onto their idealism, revel in second chances and face the future with optimism. Meanwhile, of course, your kids are going through their own upheavals and would certainly appreciate it if you could manage to be just a little less confused than they are.

CHAPTER SIX

Marriage — Your Kids Know What's Going On

Children who turn into teenagers bring a whole new dimension into your life. Surviving as a couple is no mean feat in itself, and just when you are getting out the champagne glasses, here comes the test of a lifetime!

However, it's important to remember that the state of your marriage also has an enormous impact on your children. Good, bad or indifferent, they know what's going on and react to it. The state of the marriage largely determines the climate in the home, how secure and well loved kids feel, and whether or not it's something they might consider for themselves in the future. And when marriages don't make it, that takes its toll too. People who are separated or divorced don't stop being parents.

Keeping It Afloat

First of all, don't be put off by young peoples' attitudes. Things have changed in the past decade or so. Although most teenagers will admit to a desire to marry one day, there is no longer a sense of great urgency about it. All in good time, they say, there are other priorities as well such as establishing a career, seeing the world, or simply prolonging the freedom and relative independence of singlehood.

Chances are too, that they are simply not inspired by what they see. Even when you think you're doing OK, teenagers may perceive your marriage as humdrum or perfunctory. You've spent a third of a lifetime nurturing a relationship that seems reasonably stable, caring and supportive, and they see it as boring or stultifying. Little do they know how much hard work, persistence and goodwill may have gone into keeping it afloat (and boring).

How Does It All Work Out?

The success or otherwise of a marriage is influenced by many things, not the least of which is why people got together in the first place. Experience teaches that, as a basis for an enduring relationship, the following do not rate too highly:

- Romantic love—it feels great at the time, but the rosy glow wears off fast
- A neurotic need—disappointing, because it soon becomes obvious that someone else cannot solve your personal problems
- Extenuating circumstances—the 'shot gun' wedding of yesteryear (much less popular now)

Take two highly complex individuals, each moulded by a unique upbringing and life experience, each with a full set of personal needs and expectations, and ask them to chant with sincerity, 'till death us do part'. They are somehow supposed to mesh together and make a go of it. How does it ever work out? Where is the training one needs for such a difficult job? How can it sometimes last for so long?

Of course, two people may have clung together over the years because they were too anxious to do anything else (or too tired, or 'too stuck'). But it is more likely that they had something going for them in the first place. They probably knew each other reasonably well, perceived each other without too much distortion of reality and felt sort of 'right' about it from the start.

CRISIS
PORT
WINDIES
TOO GOOD

Never Plain Sailing

Even so, making it to the middle years is commendable. Consider some of the rough spots that one has weathered along the way: the initial adjustment to intimate living, the dreadful first year, the birth of the first child, the toddlerhood of the first child and the birth of the second child, the chicken pox and head lice . . .

As you can see, the list is grossly inadequate, but the point is clear. People soon figure out that life is not about candlelit dinners and romantic strolls at dusk (well, not often anyway). This important relationship is actually conducted against a background of trivia, a kaleidoscope of mundane events and pressures such as bills, repairs, shopping, appointments and household chores.

By middle age, in fact, wedding anniversaries are being celebrated with either growing wonder or growing dismay. Friends you haven't seen for a while greet you with mock admiration, 'Good heavens, still together!' They'll want to know the secret of your success.

Is There a Secret of Success?

Who knows? Maybe you like each other. Maybe it's better than the alternative. One thing is certain, it hasn't been easy. There is no such thing as a perfectly harmonious relationship. This is, in fact, a contradiction in terms.

According to clever analysts of human behaviour, a successful marriage incorporates the following basic elements (the so called 'Four Cs'):

Conflict—a normal and necessary component of any relationship (but one requiring skill and goodwill to reach constructive solutions)

Communication—saying what you feel will not always solve problems, but it's a good place to start (few people have sufficient psychic powers to read minds); often it's *how* you say what you feel that's important too

Change—unsettling and unavoidable, but a sign of life (requires flexibility, tolerance and sensitivity to a partner's changing needs)

Commitment—an oldfashioned concept embodying such chestnuts as mutual care, concern and loyalty

There is also a place in a good marriage for mirth and merriment; for sharing responsibilities; for talking through plans, aspirations and troubles; for affection and love; and of course, for sticking it out through the bad times.

What About Now?

Marriages can get into difficulty during the middle years. Spouses may have matured at different rates, couples may gradually grow apart, or the marriage may become the focus of dissatisfaction as part of a midlife crisis. There are also powerful social forces contributing to personal discontent. For example, changing sex roles and the allure of a companionship marriage, in which equality is the key, can upset the balance, particularly in more traditional marriages.

This is the time too, when children become adolescents. If the normal, inescapable rigours of everyday life leave you emotionally drained and exhausted, bad luck, because living in close quarters with teenagers brings new stresses and novel strains. These take many forms, but at the very least, there will be:

- More encroachment on your private time (they stay up later at night and need to be taken places at weekends)
- More demands on your energy and resources (physical, emotional and financial)
- More conflicts over behaviour and rules

Your Marriage Is Affecting the Kids

Who knows what goes on behind closed doors? From the outside, it's impossible to tell what other people's marriages are like, and we should be cautious about making assumptions. A picture of joy and light might be a charade. The couple who bicker in public might actually have a very solid relationship.

Likewise, nobody can rate your marriage either. Only you know whether it's 'dawn to dusk ecstasy' or 'sheer bloody murder'. If this is the case, you'll be in no doubt at all. Chances are, however, that it falls somewhere in between these extremes, probably in one or other of two major categories. The distinction is an important one to make, because, for better or for worse, young lives are being affected.

Not Too Bad or Better

Many married couples at this stage of life will describe a relationship that's reasonable. There's a discernible amount of affection, understanding, mutual appreciation and companionship. The individuals concerned are able to feel OK about themselves and have enough personal resources to devote to their parenting tasks. This situation isn't bliss, far from it, but it provides a stable enough base from which family members can get on with their lives.

When the parents' relationship has something going for it, the kids don't need to be the entire focus of attention. This is a good thing. Why should the needs and rights of parents be totally submerged? You have your own interests and activities, separate and different from those of your offspring. Parents are people too, and recognising this is good for teenagers as well. (Growing up is actually more manageable when the oldies aren't always hovering around, sweaty and anxious, waiting for something awful to happen.)

Teenagers are generally pleased when they see their parents are prepared to work at improving their relationship. Of course, not all the means at your disposal are for their consumption. As sex researchers, Masters and Johnson told us in 1966, there's no excuse for boredom. Having a spell away from the kids can also be a rejuvenating experience, especially if the setting is romantic and there are people to wait on you. There's time to quietly concentrate on each other and, ultimately, everybody benefits.

Not Too Good or Worse

On the other hand, little comfort can be drawn from a relationship characterised by ongoing conflict, lack of communication and withdrawal. If the ingredients that go into making a reasonable marriage are missing, and there is little or no emotional support, feelings of poor self-worth and bitterness are likely to flourish. As author Michael Novak observes, 'If the quality of family life deteriorates, there is no quality of life'.

For one thing, most parental energies are caught up in coping with a difficult situation. There are various options, none of which is particularly satisfactory. Some people (brave or foolish, depending on your point of view), just put up with it. Some turn to mind-altering substances to dull the disappointment and lessen the feelings of loss. (One wonders how many unhappy marriages are actually maintained by the pharmaceutical industry.) Others embrace outside solace as compensation for their troubles at home:

- Extramarital affairs, all but the most trivial, at least, generally reflect unmet needs within a marriage
- Men typically turn to alcohol, sport or work, often escaping a troubled homelife by simply staying away from it
- Women are somewhat more likely to immerse themselves in activities and interests, frequently those of a self-improving nature, and more inclined to spend time talking out problems with friends
- Women also turn to food, often putting on weight and then spending all their money trying to lose it again

In fact, a lot of this is about struggling with stress and uncertainty and it resembles the behaviour of mixed up adolescents. There is a return to narcissism, concerns about adequacy and that uncomfortable feeling of not being in full control. A poor or deteriorating relationship is also imbued with sadness and there's really no way to hide it.

They Know What's Going On

No matter what's happening on the surface, children know when something's not quite right. More than we realise, they worry about their parents, about their health, their happiness, and increasingly, the state of their marriage. They sense what family therapists know too well, that the marital relationship is pivotal to the functioning of the family. Inevitably, this affects them in an intense and personal way.

An unhappy homelife is an enormous burden for children of any age. It is sadly reflected in their behaviour, their school work, their relationships and their general state of mind. Parents may resent being unreasonably blamed for all sorts of things to do with their kids, but there is no ducking this one. Even though it's probably nobody's fault, the consequences can be serious and far reaching, especially for teenagers, who may become seriously depressed or dramatically display their feelings.

Painful, unhappy vibes

It's no fun living in a home that's tense, uncomfortable and humourless, worse still if it's downright dangerous. Children and young adolescents of violent relationships are particularly at risk. They can become fearful, anxious and withdrawn, develop nightmares, bedwetting or other stress related symptoms, or become aggressive towards others. Even when things are less dramatic, life's not great. Teenagers soak up vibes like a sponge, and when the vibes are bad, it's like taking poison. It saps your energy and troubles your mind. But a surprising number of such kids suffer in silence, dreaming of happier places and longing for better times.

Tony was 15 when he first came to see me, unhappy about the size of his nose, his lack of friends at school and the difficulty he was having concentrating on his studies. During one of our talks, he described his parents' marriage as loveless and his homelife as barren. He said, 'We all just do our own thing. We're not connected to each other at all'. Tony also felt that no one

Great vibes

understood him and viewed the situation as unfixable. His disappointment and sadness were touching all areas of his life.

Sometimes, things can improve. Maybe Mum and Dad can get their act together somehow, and push on a little more hopefully. On the other hand, perhaps it really would be better for all concerned if they cut their losses and ended it. After all, this is easier now. Since the changes in the laws concerning divorce, divorces have skyrocketed and now all it takes to prove irretrievable breakdown is a single year's separation.

Calling It Quits

Forty to 45 per cent of marriages end in separation or divorce. The implications are complex, and for those involved, the outcomes uncertain. People outside the situation cannot always appreciate the traumas of an unworkable and destructive marriage and the relief and freedom that separation can bring.

Alternatively, people sometimes plummet headlong from an unsuccessful marriage into an unsuccessful divorce, a classic no win situation. Some people remain neurotically tied to each other even after they separate and the conflict continues indefinitely. Others embark upon divorce politely, in mutual agreement that this is for the best (although occasionally without properly thinking things through), and end up in a vicious circle of bitterness and strife. You see, even when a marriage has been awful and calling it quits is welcomed, there is still a lot to come to terms with.

Meanwhile, in the midst of these distressing games that grown-ups play, whatever the reasons, *the major losers are the kids*. For them, a disintegrating family causes a special sort of bereavement. Feelings of sadness, anger, fear, guilt and disappointment are to be expected, although teenagers often express these less openly than adults. Adjustment is most difficult, and suffering most prolonged, however, when there is ongoing acrimony and conflict. Even then there is a fervent hope that parents will be reunited. Getting caught up in parental battles, being used in 'play-offs' and being forced to make impossible choices are incredibly hard to handle.

Children from broken homes are significantly more likely to

repeat the experience themselves. Researchers have also discovered other unpalatable possibilities, especially when marital disruption is associated with serious deprivation (for example, poverty and overcrowding, inadequate care of the kids, parental illness or disability): girls are at greater risk of depression in adult life while boys are at greater risk of delinquency and criminal behaviour.

Despite the personal distress and suffering that inevitably accompany separation and divorce, parents can do a great deal to lessen the pain for their kids:

- By not being afraid to ask for counselling or guidance for the family
- By seeking similar help for themselves when they need it (self-defeating guilt and other feelings can be pretty intractable)
- By creating an open climate of communication in the home (a job for the parent who's in charge, and possibly the greatest gift a child or adolescent could receive at this time)
- By allowing them to relate lovingly to the 'missing parent' (even if this means biting one's bottom lip and declaring a truce)
- By separating problems with your partner from problems as parents; it is possible (but not necessarily easy) to work on and resolve parenting issues, and avoid dividing the kids' loyalties; although parents may not be together, and may have ongoing problems in their own relationship, they are still *parents* and always will be; perhaps the most caring act you can do for your kids, if you have separated, is to make the decision to share the responsibility of parenting together

What Does the Future Hold?

Let's end where we began, with teenage confusion about the whole business. No wonder young people are perplexed. Not only are no two marriages the same, but the outcomes are totally unpredictable.

For some people, marriage is merely a comfortable arrangement, something they've become used to, like a pair of ragged old slippers. More adventurous souls want intensity, excitement and unbridled sex. Anything less, and they're off to greener pastures. Then there are terribly unhappy people who stay unhappily together, methodically building an edifice of misery. Others want out, simply to try something different, even when the marriage has been, to all intents and purposes, reasonably happy and successful. Such is the infinite variety of human nature.

Perhaps there's another way to go. As teenagers peer warily into the misty future, a number of relationship options open up before them and marriage is merely one of them. Evidently, society has moved to the point where the family needs to be redefined (an issue to be taken up in the next chapter.)

Conclusion

If the root of all suffering lies in wanting things, we're all in big trouble. Our most basic desires and expectations constantly set us up. We want things from ourselves, we want things from each other and we want things from life itself.

Many of us, it seems, want to be married. Despite the unrest and change of the past decade, around 95 per cent of people choose to do so. Of those who divorce, two out of every three marry again. It must have something going for it. Eleanor Berman puts it simply:

> No one has yet devised a better way to serve our fundamental human needs for emotional security, the preparation of children for responsible adulthood and a framework that gives meaning and happiness to life.

Let's give up on the idea of a 'normal' family

CHAPTER SEVEN

Homelife and the Daily Grind

The family, somewhat under siege, but still the cornerstone of society, has a powerful and enduring influence on people's lives. For most children, it is the centre of their operations and it is very, very important. Someone said, 'What is most needed in the modern home is the family'. This sounds good, and raises some important questions. For example, what is a family these days?

Everybody knows that families come in all shapes and sizes; that they are special groups of people who develop unique styles of relating and coping, of showing affection and expressing outrage. How they do this, however, and where teenagers fit into the scheme of things, also bears looking at. Show me a household where the kids don't get on their parents' nerves, or where the opposite doesn't equally apply.

Getting along with each other is what life's mainly about. Since parents and teenagers have their own needs and rights, some sort of workable balance has to be arrived at. For most of us, whatever we do in the outside world, and whatever the setup at home, the people we live with are there to return to.

What Is a Family?

There's no such thing as 'the family'. Only about five in every hundred families would fit the TV image of two parents and two children, one of each sex, with the father in paid employment and the mother at home full time. Advertisers still haven't figured this out. Perhaps they just think it's the image that people still aspire to.

A family has been described as 'a group of people irrationally committed to one another's well being'. Would that this were always the case, but it's certainly the general idea. People who cohabit constitute a family system in which whatever is happening to any one, or more, individual members, affects everyone else.

Such is the rich tapestry of life, that families range from the usual or the ordinary to the interesting and bizarre. (Let's give up on the idea of *normal* right here.) There are, however, a number of readily identifiable family types which will serve as a basis for discussion:

- **Traditional**—the classical nuclear arrangement consisting of mother, father and children
- **Single Parent**—a legacy of divorce, death, chance or choice
- **Blended** (or reconstituted)—the result of 'mix and match' arrangements
- **Extended**—the multiperson (sometimes multigeneration) household, a golden fantasy from the past
- **Alternative**—various interesting combinations of adults and children

The Traditional Family

Families have become smaller. Approximately one in three children is an only child, and just over half have no sibling of the opposite sex. There's room to swing a cat, of course, but fewer people per household to turn to for solace.

Dr Judianne Denson Gerber (American anti-drug and pornography campaigner) has described the nuclear family as 'society's act of violence against itself'. Isolated, struggling and stressed, and much too mobile for the good of children, it often falls far short of the ideal it has been portrayed to be. When community supports are lacking (or seem hard to get at) and relatives are few and far between, 'nuclear' parents bear the full weight of parenthood on their sagging

Nuclear family: Mobile, isolated, struggling, stressed

shoulders. And when teenagers are being difficult, which is not all that unusual, it can feel an especially heavy load to bear.

Nevertheless, many parents cope reasonably well with this arrangement, work hard, raise their kids and rarely give a thought to the alternatives. It's probably the only sort of family they've known. But it's a mistake to think that this is the norm—only 28 per cent of Australians live in nuclear families, and in future years will comprise an increasingly small proportion.

The Single Parent Family

What about when there's only one set of shoulders at home? Nobody's going to pretend this is easier, but it's certainly not uncommon:

- A high proportion of children lose a parent (through separation, divorce or death) by the age of 15
- A higher proportion of children lives in a single person household (usually with a female parent or relative)
- At some time a large number of parents will be a single parent

A single parent household comes about when a parent has never married, a spouse dies or a married couple split up. How well or badly things work out will depend upon the nature and circumstances of the separation, the emotional stability of the remaining parent, and the quality of family and community supports. If the other parent is still around, that is, not dead or out of town, the relationship of the ex-spouses and how the kids fit into this are the most crucial factors.

It is important to realise, however, that adolescents are devastated by a loss of this magnitude, and the early stages in particular are likely to be terrible. They can be aggressive and lash out (mostly at the accessible parent) or become angrily sullen and withdrawn. This can be very difficult to handle for the suddenly single person who, one way or another, already has a lot to contend with:

- For one thing, personal grief can consume virtually all of one's resources
- If there's divorce in the air, the exhausting legal merry go round can add immeasurably to the drama and strife
- The custodial parent (usually the mother) is often faced with financial difficulties, a lack of practical assistance and little moral support

Things are not necessarily very good for the missing parent either. If it's the father (which it usually is), he is more likely than his married counterpart to need treatment for mental health problems. From his children's point of view, the most important thing he can do is to keep telling them he loves them. They will want to hear this. After all, even if he's not living with them, he is still going to be their parent.

For teenagers, there are often divided loyalties, and they can become extremely skilled at playing parents off against each other. Sometimes, through difficult behaviour or symptoms of illness, kids are expressing a sad and desperate hope for reconciliation. They think, 'Maybe, if I'm enough of a problem, they'll have to get back together again to sort it out'. Of course, it rarely works out that way.

A teenager in a single parent home (or a younger child, for that matter), may become 'parentified' and take on the role of the missing parent. Having too much responsibility can speed up adolescence and rob such young people of the opportunity to enjoy these years. They are unable to develop more gradually, as was intended, or sometimes even to take part in normal teenage activities or experimentation. This does not always have serious consequences, although children who are affected this way do appear more prone to depression.

At 16, the law permits teenagers to choose where they live. It is very common for them to choose to live with the other parent at this time (especially the first born, who tends to pine most for the family that was). This relatively dramatic change of arrangements can be quite disturbing for all concerned.

The evidence suggests that it can take up to 5 years or more for the dust to settle. Eventually, as the necessary adjustments are made, life can get, more or less, back to normal, whatever that is. Without doubt, a parent raising children or teenagers alone can be extremely effective, cope with the extra demands, and allow the kids to be kids. The family is then able to push on, diminished but undaunted.

The Blended Family

When people remarry and take children with them, things can get pretty complicated. As one teenager explained with a resigned air, 'I've got one proper brother, two step sisters and there's half a something else on the way'. When it comes to figuring out uncles, aunts and cousins, most people give up.

If you're thinking of getting into this situation, stop watching television immediately. Those ghastly, sickly sweet family situation comedies will have you feeling inferior in no time. They model love, harmony and joy and the successful resolution of all crises. Real life isn't like that.

Let's take one step back, to before the 'deed' is done. Teenagers get used to the way things are in a single parent household. When all is going well, they know their place and pull their weight. So one can forgive them for being less than thrilled when a parent's lover 'gets the nod' and great upheavals are set in train. Or when there is a succession of part time lovers which can really make roles confusing.

I know of one family in which a woman underwent a complete personality change. Having been an excessively devoted and self-sacrificing type of mother to her four children, she eventually broke away from what was, for her, an unsatisfactory marriage. Suddenly free and head over heels in love with somebody new, she became a star struck kid, totally besotted by her gallant lover. (Another sort of return to adolescence perhaps?) A frenzied courtship left the kids, for the first time in their lives, often in the hands of somebody new. The change in their mother's behaviour and attitude, let alone the marriage that soon followed, left the kids completely bewildered.

Certain teenage reactions are to be expected:

- For most kids, the new situation is likely to provoke a new bout of grief, as it puts an end, once and for all, to any remaining hope of a reconciliation for their parents
- For a teenage girl, even coping with the reality of a mother's reawakened sexuality can be difficult, and occasionally leads to sexually provocative behaviour (for example, in a competitive relationship with mother for the attention of her new partner)
- For older adolescents in particular, there is a change of role to adjust to; having been the special male or special female in the family, someone has arrived to take this over (hence the feeling of competitiveness experienced by both boys and girls)
- Many teenagers speak of a resentment of the new partner and of a desire to oust him or her from the house

So new step parents don't have it easy at all. They want to make inroads with the children they haven't fathered (or mothered), but this can be a slow process. There's the possibility that they've gone into a second marriage without having completely worked through the difficulties related to the one that's failed, and often have 'magical thinking' about how wonderful things are going to be now. It takes time for children to accept and trust a new parent figure (especially if emotional traumas are fresh), and teenagers can make life very awkward indeed.

It's also normal to feel protective towards one's own children (or guilty about doing things with your new spouse's offspring when yours live elsewhere). Petty jealousies and resentments are pretty usual. Blended families can work out extremely well, although some difficulties and compromises will simply have to be lived with.

The Extended Family

Families can be extended in all sorts of ways: Grandma or Uncle Fred can come along and stay indefinitely (perhaps because of old age, illness or becoming widowed); maybe they already own the house and you live with them; another whole family can move in downstairs (because they're refurbishing their own home and it's too cold to live in a caravan).

The image that comes most readily to mind, of course, is of three or more generations of people, all living together in glorious peace and supportive harmony. Part of the myth surrounding extended families, and the reason that people in nuclear families think they're missing out on something, is the idea that 'the others' (meaning, not the biological parents) will help discipline and care for the kids. The notion of sharing these roles and responsibilities is attractive, is it not? Perhaps, at times, it really does work out just like that, and family members are imbued with feelings of esteem and well being.

But often it doesn't. One does hear, not uncommonly, of tensions, intrusions and strife. A lot depends on how the family got to be extended and on the degree to which roles and expectations have been clearly sorted out. If elderly grandparents (or other relatives) know that they make an important contribution by their willingness to babysit, for example, but otherwise are *not* expected to behave like a parent, well and good. The alternative, where nobody knows who's supposed to be doing what, can get pretty messy.

The grownups involved must also be able to relate to one another in a mature way, adult to adult. It's when teenagers see

Stereotype (somewhat outdated and loosely defined) roles within an extended family

their parents not being able to stand up to their own parents, that trouble can occur. In all likelihood, the kids will simply force their sandwiched folks to take charge. (You can see this happening, in fact, even when grandparents are merely paying a visit.)

The Alternative Family

There are many other styles of family living. Sometimes they work out, sometimes they don't. The following possibilities are examples of what is available:

- **The commune**—based on principles of co-operation and goodwill, and varying from loosely organised shanty towns to more stable groups of committed families (as in the Israeli Kibbutzim)
- **The 'groupie' family**—consisting generally of youngish people who live together under the same roof sharing incomes, ideas, tasks and other things as well
- **The homosexual family**—a family with two or more 'parents' and one or more kids
- **The 'stretched' family**—arrangements in which other families or single people provide some sort of support, either on site (as when a family takes in a helpful boarder) or through meeting regularly to share problems, exchange services, and perhaps enjoy leisure pursuits together

Alternative families can provide problems for adolescents, who basically do not like being different to their peers. Also, when the boundaries between people are less clear cut than usual, as they often are in these situations, kids may fear that their sexual impulses will get out of control. Where the parenting adults are of the same sex (usually women but occasionally men), there may be role confusion. Overall, for teenagers in alternative families, it can be more difficult to grow up and become independent. Sometimes things simply become too difficult to deal with and they opt out by running away.

Getting Along Together

A family is clearly different things to different people. But essentially, it is an organised group held together by the power of its dominant members. When children reach adolescence, there may be questions raised as to who the dominant members actually are, but the point remains valid. Like all groups, a family has certain basic needs. These are:

- An identity—usually determined by such things as your family name, how neat you keep the garden and other special traits
- A place to protect its resources—your dwelling, however humble that may be
- A committed membership—you, the kids and whoever else is currently in residence
- Effective leadership—hopefully yours
- Inner cohesion—related entirely to how members get along together
- A value system and rules governing conduct
- A sense of history and connectedness—this helps particularly when birthdays and religious holidays are being celebrated

It is also nice for a family, like any other group, to have a sense of purpose and direction. This comes about when the leadership has goals and aspirations (such as what to do when the kids leave home). But how it feels to belong to a family, largely depends on what's happening within those four walls, on the presence or absence of inner cohesion. How are people getting along together? What is their degree of co-operation, mutual understanding and goodwill?

Communication Is the Key

Communication is the lubricant that enables people to get along together. It is really difficult to overstate its importance. Of course, one's style of relating is pretty well established by the time children turn into teenagers. Nevertheless, it can come as an awful shock when things start to go off the rails.

Ever wondered why teenagers find parents such a pain in the neck? No matter what they say or do, poor old Mum or Dad just never seem to get it right. For example, a 15 year old girl comes sobbing to her mother, saying that the earrings she wanted to wear to a party are nowhere to be found. Her mother says, 'Never mind, dear. I'll let you borrow some of mine'. Daughter storms out, slamming the door, saying, 'Thanks a lot. You really don't care, do you !'

Many a parent has looked to heaven and wondered, 'What did I say wrong?' Where parents and teenagers are concerned, unfortunately, the message sent is frequently not the message received. The complexities of human communication have been neatly summed up as follows: 'I know that you believe you understand what you think I said, but I'm not sure you realise that what you heard is not what I meant'.

Perceptions can differ so widely, that misunderstandings are virtually inevitable. As psychologist and author, Haim Ginott, explains, 'Help is perceived as interference, concern as babying, advice as bossing'. At our dinner table recently, I politely asked my teenage daughter to kindly pass the pepper. Her mumbled reply sounded like, 'What did your other slaves die of?' When a simple enquiry is an interrogation; a simple observation, an unfeeling intrusion; and a simple request, a monumental imposition, what do you do?

It doesn't appear to pose as much difficulty in the other direction. Teenagers just know what not to tell their parents (smokescreen communication). This is a skill they cherish, as if their survival depended on it. They develop a sixth sense about the sort of response particular information is likely to bring, (especially when it involves behaviour that comes perilously close to the limits set). They think, 'Why buy trouble?' So, when a kid says literally nothing for days on end, you know something's up.

Another communication dilemma facing parents is how much to share one's personal problems. In many situations, openness is a good thing (since they generally know what's going on anyway), but to overburden your offspring with essentially grownup worries may be unfair.

Partly a Matter of Time

So much is written about why and how parents should relate to their teenage children. It's good stuff usually, hammering the importance of bolstering self-esteem and staying cool under duress. But less attention is given to when all this is supposed to happen.

There is a saying that 'the best inheritance a parent can give his children is a few minutes of his time each day'. It's true. In our busy world, having a little time, some undivided attention, makes a child of any age feel wanted and important. Even the most gorgeous and extravagant gifts cannot compensate for this. In fact, being together is a prerequisite for chatting together, is it not?

A mother of two young adolescents describes her family's homelife as follows:

> The kids come home from school, have a quick bite and do their homework. After dinner, we go to bed. My husband usually comes home much later. On weekends, they want to be with their friends. Of course, sometimes we're all together, watching television like zombies.

Perhaps she should be pleased that they spend any time together at all. When everybody's rushing around, meaningful discussions are likely to be very rare, unless some special effort is made. Some families take active steps to enable communication as a group and this too has its merits. There are a number of possibilities:

- You can organise a regular meeting at which everybody gets to have a say; whether this is tightly chaired or more of a friendly free for all is a question of preferred style
- Families more taken with bureaucratic procedures might prefer an anonymous suggestion box, the contents of which will serve as the basis for a thorough discussion from time to time
- Others simply prefer to deal with issues as they arise (frequently, it would seem, over dinner)

On the other hand, family members may simply have a capacity to tune in to each other. The point is that people's ideas and views need to be taken seriously. Whether you're 6 years old or 46 years old is not the issue. The people who communicate well, at any age, are those who know how to listen. There is probably no single skill more valuable in this regard.

Between Parents and Teenagers

It would be very unusual for fathers and mothers not to want good things for their kids. Whether in relation to appearance, sport, education or future success, parents can be motivated by two powerful desires:

- For their children to do as well as or better than they did or
- For their children to do what they were unable to do

This may be called the 'achievement imperative' and is either good or bad for the teenager depending on degree. There's a fine line sometimes between setting a standard and encouraging effort, on the one hand, and coercing with heavy pressure and unrealistic expectations (usually because of one's own needs) on the other. It's important to know the difference and worthwhile thinking about what your motives are next time you're running up and down the sidelines of a football field or putting pressure on your daughter to stay in all weekend to study.

Families also vary enormously in the way they express affection. Some families are extremely cuddlesome, while others might prefer a firm handshake at bedtime. Touching is very powerful. Children who grow up in a physically demonstrative and warm home will probably raise their own kids the same way. Of course, there are also many subtle and non-physical ways to indicate affection. The caring things we say and do clearly convey the message as well.

An individual parent and an individual teenager have to get along together too. Relatively little research has been done on this, although it is evident that special relationships can develop in each of four directions:

Mothers and daughters have something in common: they're the same sex. This should be good news. However, as her own biological clock ticks on, a mother has to deal with her feelings concerning her daughter's emerging sexuality, and this is not all that easy.

During the early teenage years, girls will gain the distance they need. They do this by seeking privacy, usually through a frequent withdrawal to their bedroom. However, if lines of communication are open, they will seek closeness and support when they need it. A daughter who has been more or less 'missing' for days, can suddenly turn up in desperate need of some item of mother's clothing. (This doesn't work quite so well in reverse—teenage girls do not want their mothers to be too 'with it'.) It will have its ups and downs, but in due course, there is much comfort and enjoyment to be drawn from this relationship on both sides.

Mothers generally have aspirations for their daughters. The traditional 'get yourself a wealthy and successful man, settle down and have children' is probably still pretty common, although many mothers might now prefer that young women consolidate their identities, gain a secure career and obtain for themselves a capacity for independence.

With **mothers and sons**, it can go either way. A boy going through puberty can be pretty hard to take, particularly in regard

Mothers and daughters have something in common

...he may simply pick her up...

to his personal hygiene, smutty humour and physical awkwardness. But emotional distance and physical closeness are not mutually exclusive. If a teenage boy wants to get close to his mum, he may simply pick her up (at which time her best response is simply to be incredibly impressed by his marvellous strength).

Sometimes a mother looks to a teenage son for the closeness she is not experiencing with her husband (whether or not he's physically present). This can give rise to a special, stable and not overly healthy twosome within the family. It is not an incestuous relationship, just one in which two people are extremely sensitive to each other's needs and feelings. However, it can make it more difficult for the adolescent boy to separate in a normal way, and may contribute to other difficulties such as refusing to go to school.

Relationships between **fathers and sons** are usually less intense and personal than those between mothers and daughters, and more competitive. This is thought to be because certain things are important to them both, simply because they're male: having strength and agility, being attractive to women (both within and outside the family), and being economically successful. As boys flex their newly grown muscles, dads can expect to be tested out in all areas.

Boys are very fortunate to have a confident and committed father who can handle this with tolerance and good humour. It has been called the 'loving fight' and without it, mutual respect is lost and a boy's self-esteem is likely to suffer. Fathers who are struggling with their own identity issues (the midlife crisis) may either opt out or overreact in a very heavy handed way. On occasion, an adolescent boy's emotional and behavioural problems can be traced to this cause.

Father and daughter relationships are special too. A dad's approval, affirmation and affection contribute enormously to a teenage girl's self-concept and her developing confidence in dealing with other men. According to recent research, just having a father around helps to protect her against the risk of future depression and relationship problems.

Most fathers handle the flirtatious behaviour of their teenage daughters with knowing reserve, or their withdrawal from closeness with understanding. Of course, when other males start to take an interest in his 'little princess', paternal shackles can rapidly rise. Fathers are notoriously protective of their daughters and can be overly restrictive at times, in an effort to restrain their developing sexuality. Girls in immigrant families often experience particular problems here, which can add immeasurably to the stress of growing up (particularly since they are often egged on by their non-ethnic friends).

...dads can expect to be tested out... ...when other males start to take an interest...

Sibling Strife

Not all kids fight with their siblings, only about 99 per cent of them. The word 'sibling', literally means 'little relation', but it also refers to someone older, who can show you the way, or someone around the same age (which means trouble, in anybody's language). I know a 15 year old boy who infuriates his sister by constantly saying, 'Come here, girlie'. He loves the reaction he gets.

Ultimately, there is likely to be a special sibling bond, something that parents like to see. But during adolescence, this can get extremely stretched. Why do teenagers frequently not get along with their 'partners in crime'? The factors involved include the following:

- An excrutiating sensitivity to any comment or glance in reference to their bodies or embarrassed interest in the opposite sex; my 11 year old daughter (who seems to spend hours doing her hair) ribs her older brother about his small crop of juicy pimples and he retaliates with, 'And you love yourself, don't ya?'
- An exceptional degree of physical gratification related to pushing and shoving; so when she squeals, 'he keeps touching me', she might not actually want to be rescued
- An exquisite sense of fair play coupled with a climate of constant inequity; have you noticed how kids measure things?; we line up four glasses and pour milk—woe betide if the levels do not turn out exactly equal!; one of them does mental estimates of the relative value of birthday presents
- An exhausting and ruthless struggle for scarce parental attention (usually when parents are absolutely exhausted and have practically nothing to give)
- An extraordinary resistance to any adult inspired measure to prevent or stop it

You can hurt inside when kids are constantly at each others' throats. Especially when it's occurring in a confined space, murder seems entirely reasonable. On a long car trip (or any other disastrous holiday), for example, you may feel inclined to put

... an exceptional degree of physical gratification related to pushing and shoving

them out on the footpath and let them fight there forever. No one is ever wise enough to know who really starts a sibling fracas, so level headed parents do their best to butt out. They don't always succeed.

Some Teenagers Have Problem Parents

One day, a 10 year old girl announced with importance to her family, 'Forget about strangers, it's fathers you've got to be careful of'. An important message was getting through, although her own dad was momentarily less than comfortable. Not every parent is an abuser. Yet, when a father exploits his position of power and authority, for example, and draws his daughter into sexual activity with him, things have gone badly wrong.

There is no doubt that feelings of mutual attraction exist between fathers and daughters, but acting upon them in this way is illegal, a clear betrayal of trust, and causes fear and humiliation.

The experience of incest (which is far more common than we could possibly imagine) is often associated with long standing emotional problems for the girl.

There is increasing community awareness of child sexual abuse (the most significant kind of abuse where teenagers are concerned) and, ever so slowly, the health, welfare and legal systems are trying to sort out how best to deal with it. There's a long way to go, because it's a wretched and apparently growing problem. Consider these depressing facts about sexual abuse:

- Its incidence is grossly underestimated (because a majority of children and teenagers, through fear of being disbelieved, do not report it); workers in the field currently believe that a frighteningly high number of girls under 18 have experienced an unwanted sexual incident; boys are sexually abused too, although it comes to light less commonly
- It is perpetrated by a family member (or other older person for whom the child has positive feelings) in most cases
- It is more likely to happen in blended families
- It involves the abuse of different children in a family, more commonly than abuse of one only
- It is generally secret and ongoing
- It can cause puzzling symptoms (such as abdominal pain or strange turns), emotional or school difficulties, and problems of future sexual adjustment

This is a highly complex situation and not one that is likely to be resolved without expert, professional help. Unfortunately, one cannot assume support or sympathy for the victim, which greatly adds to the difficulties of sorting it out. Girls who ultimately reveal their experiences of sexual abuse are often faced with scepticism, hostility or disdain, even by family members. Forensic examinations, police interviews and appearances in court greatly compound their trauma. While offenders still mostly get off, the pendulum is swinging more towards the needs and rights of the abused and there is much greater concern about protection.

Back to the Daily Grind

On a somewhat lighter note, let's take a brief look at the mad rat race many of us are caught up in. Like frenzied rats, we scurry back and forth, day after day, building mountains out of mole-hills or even larger mountains out of mountains. Our energies and resources are all but consumed by work. As I hinted at earlier, family life is often about 'working, working, working'. This goes equally for fathers and mothers:

Working Fathers

These have the most plausible alibi in the world for neglecting their family: 'But I'm only doing it for you.' No one will deny that there are pressures and responsibilities involved, particular-ly when you're the only income earner. But the personal losses can mount up and, especially if your spouse is at home full time, empathy might be in short supply.

This is not only because there's practically nothing as thank-less as full time housework, but also because the man seems to have the best of both worlds. He has: the stimulation of an exter-nal setting, people to relate to (both male and female), a gener-ally structured environment, clear expectations and tangible rewards. Then he comes home to hot food and clean clothes.

Working fathers also inspire the ire of their children, partly because they're not around, and partly because when they are around, they're not really there. Preoccupations of the mind are not conducive to close and comfortable relationships. So, here we have the horns of a dilemma. Dad gives at the office, as he

... the most plausible alibi in the world...

must, and returns to the fold, tired, cranky and off the air. Balancing the needs and pressures of both work and family is never easy.

Working Mothers

Mothers who work, however, are worse off still. They have to maintain two jobs, and somehow do justice to both. Fathers are increasingly sharing domestic tasks, some are participating more fully in bringing up children, which is even better. But in more traditional relationships, where the children are concerned, responsibilities still rest mainly with the mother. The ideal, of course, is where mothers and fathers both maintain one and a half jobs each rather than mothers carrying the burden of two.

Working mothers (particularly full timers), can end up chasing their tail. They have less free time (more likely none) and less vigour and energy. They often feel less in touch with the kids and guilty when their home runs less than smoothly. A husband's resentment adds insult to injury.

Mothers who work: ...maintaining two jobs and somehow do justice to both

Pitching In

There's only one rational solution. Everybody has to 'pitch in', which brings us, finally, to the touchy subject of household chores. Families need to set priorities and decide together, what's important and who needs to do what.

For example, in homes with one parent or with two who both work, the family might agree to things being somewhat less than 'trim, taut and terrific'. Of course, some people really thrive in creative squalor (and have the advantage that burglars think someone else's been there already). Even so, Mum is not superhuman, and there are certain tasks she should definitely not take on. These include: picking up other people's dirty clothing; making other people's beds; always thinking up what's for dinner; doing all the shopping single-handed; ironing anything that's not hers.

Despite having four sets of extra hands in our family, my wife and I are not impressed with the value of elaborate rosters (we tried it once!). When help is needed, whether it's to set the table for dinner or babysit our youngest child, we simply ask for it. Generally, this seems to work well. Certain jobs, however, are obligatory: putting their own dirty clothes in the washing basket (anything that's not there doesn't get washed), putting their own washing away when it's returned to them clean and folded and tidying up their bedrooms at least once a week.

In some families, kids are expected to prepare meals, do the shopping and take on the lion's share of household cleaning. Under certain circumstances, there's probably no alternative. But young people need some leisure time and are quick to complain, if, as they see it, they are being treated unfairly. One hot summer's day, lathered in sweat, I was stuggling with the lawnmower in our neglected back garden, when each of my four children came to offer assistance. I was delighted at their care and concern. Only later did I discover that they'd been sent by their mother—'Go and help your father. He looks like he's about to die'.

Conclusion

Families are invariably interesting and incredibly important. There's always a lot going on, not the least of which, is the development and moulding of young lives. Hopefully a place of dignity, respect and trust, 'an oasis of joy and hope', a family should also provide a safe and predictable environment. For teenagers, the family home is the security base from which they take off to check out the world. It is like an aircraft carrier, always there to welcome them back when they return.

AN APPLE A DAY

Coke is IT!
BIG CHIPS

CHAPTER EIGHT

Corn Chips and Chocolate

We are blessed, in the West, with a relative abundance of food. What's more, the subject of nutrition is constantly being written about in magazines and books, the health food industry is booming and the importance of weight control and healthy eating is virtually on everybody's lips. And almost everyone knows something about anorexia nervosa, (the 'slimmer's disease') and that there are good reasons for concern about chronic constipation, obesity, and high blood cholesterol.

While parents may worry about these things, most teenagers seem blissfully unconcerned. Their entire approach to eating is generally one of breathtaking disregard for proper nutrition. They love snacking, skipping meals and junk food. If kids had their way, they'd probably try to live on Coca Cola, chips and chocolate. What's more, to the chagrin of the nutritional purists among us, they'd probably survive.

How worried should we be about all this? There's clearly more to it than potential threats to health and life. For parents and kids alike, there are also aggravations and conflicts to contend with.

What Is Healthy Eating?

Health authorities have been hammering away at us about the basics of good nutrition for some time now, so the message should be getting through. In a nutshell, we need to be eating more complex carbohydrate foods (wholegrain breads and cereals, fruit, vegetables etc.) and limiting animal protein and fat. As 10 to 20 per cent of us are genetically predisposed to developing high blood pressure on a high salt diet, we should be cutting down there too. And despite a clever marketing response by the sugar industry to falling consumption figures, we do eat too much simple sugar for our basic good. The basis of a healthy diet for all ages is simply moderation, variety and balance.

What Are the Major Worries?

Let's get right into the most worrisome issues associated with adolescent nutrition. Young people are susceptible to a range of diet related health problems, most (but not all) of which are well known, some of which are potentially dangerous, and practically all of which are preventable. Parents certainly worry, and for good reason, particularly when kids are too fat or too thin.

Too Fat

There are scientific ways to tell whether someone is genuinely obese or merely overweight. But in practice, if you look too fat, you probably are. A growing number of school children are thought to be carrying too much fat. This problem is definitely on the rise. Really obese kids have around an 80 per cent chance of becoming obese adults, which puts them at risk for a large number of medical disorders.

We still don't know exactly why obesity occurs in some people and not in others, but there is always a genetic component. One must be predisposed to it, otherwise it would make no sense at all that food affects different people in different ways, why some individuals seem immune to every culinary self-indulgence, while others gain weight on the smell of a pizza. On top of that, however, the equation involving eating on the one hand, and physical activity on the other, gets out of 'sync' in the most obvious way—too much of the former and not enough of the latter. It is often a matter of continuing to eat beyond our needs, our undoing in terms of gaining excess weight.

During adolescence, there is an increase in the number and size of fat cells. What we used to call puppy fat, however, is just fat, and fat gained is unlikely to spontaneously disappear. Overweight teenagers generally fall into one (or more) of the following three categories:

- Certain susceptible kids are vulnerable to gaining excess weight during puberty, simply by eating more food than their bodies need. The problem is predominantly one of inappropriate eating habits, and the more fat gained in this way, the more difficult it is to shift as time goes by. Normally, increasing height or a change of habits should see this sorted out. Growing teenagers have a chance to grow into their weight, as it were.
- Some fat teenagers have inherited their obesity. It's a problem that shows up early in life and responds little (if at all) to weight reduction diets. For such kids, maintaining weight and learning to live with it is the name of the game.
- Not infrequently, weight gain occurs in children or adolescents who are under stress or unhappy. The root cause here is psychological, with high energy food being used as solace. The best way to overcome this is to look at the overall situation rather than merely at the scales or what passes between the lips.

By the way, if a child or teenager is growing normally, it is a complete waste of time to go around looking for a medical cause. Despite the community myth, obesity is hardly ever due to 'the glands'. It is also unreasonable to believe that all fat young people are unhappy or in emotional strife—they may not be. However, other kids can be pretty rotten to 'fatties', and getting miserable may lead to eating even more comfort food, thus setting up a typical vicious circle.

The very best treatment for teenage obesity is prevention before adolescence, an important goal for any family to have. However, if your teenager is currently overweight, all is not lost. But don't expect miracles. A fat boy turned up to see me once with a request for help to become thin by August so that he could more comfortably join the other kids at the beach. Unfortunately, that was only 3 weeks away! Fat accumulates slowly and steadily, and that's the way it will go. It cannot be rubbed or melted off, and there is no known way to lose it from specific parts of the body (as many girls might wish).

Health professionals more or less agree on the following if kids want to lose weight:

- Without motivation, forget it!
- A combination of diet and physical activity is likely to be more effective than either alone; less time spent in front of the TV and more time pursuing something energetic like skateboarding or roller skating is a good idea
- Fad diets and meal replacement diets are not recommended—most cause a loss of body water but do little to decrease the body's fat stores
- Appetite suppressant drugs are also out for this age group—they are habit forming and (as with adults) any weight loss achieved would not be sustained after they were ceased
- Behaviour modification techniques (diaries, rewards and the like) may work for a while, although older adolescents find them a bit demeaning
- Young teenagers enjoy and benefit from a group approach; they stand to gain improved knowledge and mental attitude from well run programmes (even if, in the short term, they stay fat)

Too Thin

No one can say exactly what normal eating behaviour is, but hiding food behind the sofa, purposely throwing up, taking lots of laxatives and rushing around like a lunatic would not be included. These behaviours directed towards losing or controlling body weight are becoming more common. According to Australian studies, one in every 100 school age girls over 13 has the slimmer's disease, anorexia nervosa, and around one in twenty

The major worries: Too fat or too thin

young women have the binge eating disorder, bulimia nervosa and both are on the increase in the UK. Both can occur in boys but are less common and have a less favourable outlook.

Social pressures can partly be blamed for why eating disorders happen. Dieting is in vogue; in women's magazines over the past two decades, articles about dieting have increased threefold; an American study noted that *Playboy* centrefolds have become progressively thinner, reflecting the body form currently most desired by men; emaciated and hollow cheeked clothing models litter our fashionable department stores. Wherever girls look, the message is that being thin is in.

No wonder so many girls (more than half of all 12 year olds, in fact) enter puberty wanting to be thinner, victims to media pressure that makes them feel inadequate, even at the very threshold of womanhood. As discussed in Chapter 1, Nature decrees for pubertal girls, a normal increase in the amount of fat on thighs and buttocks—how sad that so many girls resent it. In Australia, research suggests that at least 50 per cent of girls in the senior years of high school (and a quarter of the boys) are on some form of diet!

With increased recognition of eating disorders has come a greater understanding of what makes certain young people vulnerable to them. While the broader influences are clearly relevant to the increasing trend, the essential ingredient for the individual concerned is a struggle for personal control. Psychologically, the two disorders differ somewhat, with anorexics seemingly not wanting to grow up and bulimics (who are usually older) not handling being grown up too well.

Anorexia nervosa typically occurs in a perfectionistic, achieving and previously well adjusted child. It may start insidiously, often after a chance remark about weight or fatness, but the end result is that dieting gets out of control. The main characteristics are as follows:

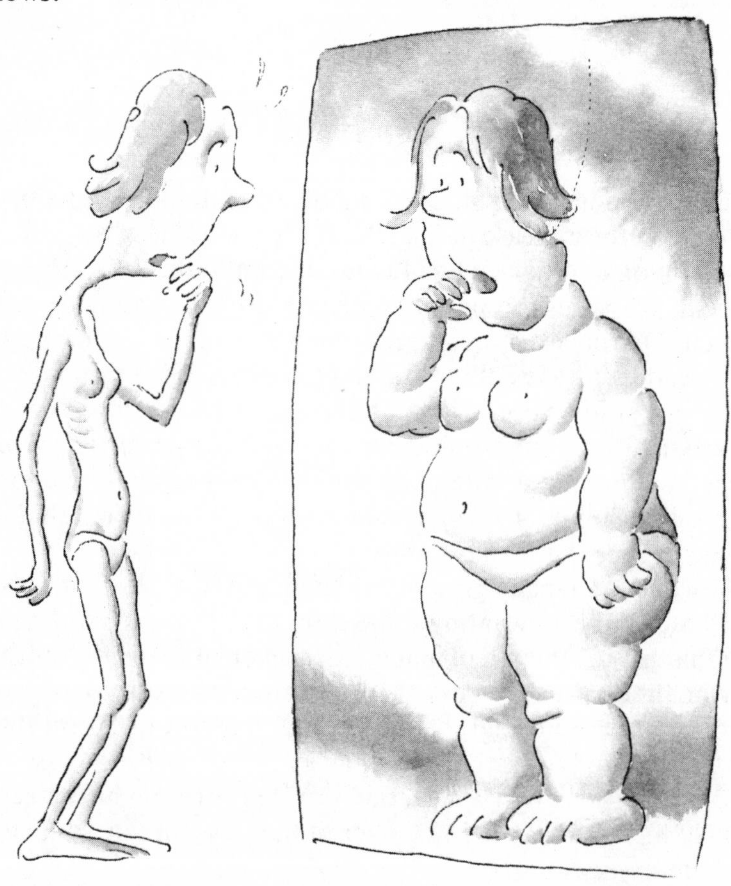

- Extreme weight loss—20 to 25 per cent of body weight—in the absence of any physical illness (this usually happens over 6 to 12 months)
- A preoccupation with body size and shape and a relentless pursuit of thinness, more or less to the exclusion of all normal concerns of adolescence
- A love of preparing food for other people, with innumerable ways of avoiding eating it themselves; an apparent belief that lettuce is a nutritious food (the 'lettuce test')
- Frenetic activity ('hooked on exercise') or other weight losing behaviours such as self-induced vomiting or laxative use
- Loss of periods and, at an advanced stage, the development of fine, downy hair over the entire body surface
- An apparent lack of concern about appearance and continued complaints about a protruding tummy or fat thighs
- A risk of death from prolonged fasting or purging, or from a direct suicide attempt (related to severe depression); overall, suicide is certainly the most common cause of death

A person with **bulimia nervosa**, on the other hand, is usually of average weight or slightly overweight and experiences a repeated compulsion to eat large amounts of high calorie food. Abdominal pain, falling asleep or self-induced vomiting usually end the binge. Typically, a bulimic attempts to resist doing this and has fears about not being able to stop voluntarily. He or she tends to be secretive and to feel guilty and often feels very depressed after a binge.

Family relationships are relevant in both these conditions, particularly in anorexia nervosa. People who are too close and caring and who tend to avoid conflict, unwittingly create an environment in which a young person may react in this way. What then follows is 'a self-destructive struggle for independence accompanied by personal despair, low self-esteem and a fear of proceeding with personal development.' Expert, professional help is urgently needed.

Parents can help in the following ways:

Bulimia nervosa: ...repeated compulsion to eat

- By recognising that something's going on and thinking about the possibility of anorexia nervosa when kids start to lose weight; the next step is to approach someone who can advise where to get help
- By not being too preoccupied with food and not letting the dinner table become a battleground
- By encouraging independence and personal responsibility in their teenagers, that is, allowing them to grow up

From Tooth Decay to Anaemia

Unhealthy eating puts teenagers at risk in a number of other ways too. Here are a few more concerns:

- Dental cavities continue to represent a potent source of personal anguish, with the incidence of tooth decay rising in direct proportion to the amount of sugar consumed
- A surprising number of children and teenagers eats no fruit or vegetables at all, so it should come as no surprise that these kids

are constipated; (for reasons that are not understood, eating more dietary fibre decreases the overall risk of cancer of the large bowel, and eating more fruit decreases the risk of cancer of the stomach)

- Teenage girls run the risk of becoming anaemic or (less likely) developing brittle bones, if their diets are deficient in iron or calcium respectively
- Increased blood fats and high blood pressure do occur in genetically susceptible adolescents, putting them at risk for coronary artery disease in later life
- There seems to be a group of children, including teenagers, in whom the ingestion of food colourings and other additives is associated with irritability, restlessness and sleep disturbance (this can usually be sorted out by doctors or nutritionists with the appropriate expertise)
- The high consumption of alcohol by young people is a major contributor to adolescent loss of life

Eat Your Greens or Go to Bed

Teenagers do most of their eating at home and away from home. I make this apparently ridiculous point, because it is relevant to parental involvement and influence. As the adolescent years roll on (whether the kids like your chicken soup or not), more and more of the food they consume will be away from your nurturing impulses and prying eyes—and that's why you worry.

Mum, What's to Eat?

Adolescents have absolutely voracious appetites, particularly during puberty. They eat constantly, and practically anything in sight. If you stock up on food for the week, say on Saturday, chances are you'll be 'cleaned out' by Sunday evening. And it's not just your kids: if friends stay over on Saturday night, you may have to eat out for breakfast.

Most parents, family budget permitting, handle this pretty well. After all, short of putting padlocks on the fridge and pantry, what can you do? Rapidly growing teenagers have enormous nutritional requirements, and if they play sport as well as growing, even more. An incredible 16 000 kilojoules of energy a day might actually be needed. (Of course, less active adolescents need less, but might be inclined to consume that much anyway.)

Household conflicts over food are more likely to be about what kids don't, or won't, eat. From the age of 8 or 9, children are starting to understand the concept of death and may become extremely concerned about the poor little creatures that provide us with protein foods. One of my own teenagers has recently gone off meat. Her special look that says 'how could you possibly eat that?' is making life a bit uncomfortable for the carnivores she lives with. Young people can also take up other fads, declare a moratorium on bananas, or refuse to eat anything else.

All of this can drive parents crazy. If you've slaved for hours over a hot stove (or struggled with complicated microwave dials), knockbacks can be disappointing. Perhaps you grew up under strict instructions to eat everything on the plate ('or you can just sit there all night'), an approach that is definitely out of vogue now. People, including adolescents, are entitled to have different tastes, wants and needs and, to some extent, these ought to be accommodated. Making choices is, after all, a normal and important part of growing up. Anyway, according to scientific reports, screaming rows at the dinner table achieve little more than the diminished absorption of food.

Lots of children miss breakfast on one or more days of the school week. For these children, breakfast consists of only a drink. Teenage girls are the guiltiest here, skipping breakfast about twice as often as boys. Many say it's a matter of simply not feeling hungry in the

morning or running out of time. Others skip breakfast in the misguided belief that it will help them control their weight. It doesn't, mostly because they get hungry and eat more (often junk food) at other meals. Furthermore, fasting has been shown to impair intellectual performance, which means that it really is harder to concentrate on school work with nothing in your stomach (an argument that may or may not have the desired effect).

In some families mealtimes don't exist at all. Have you heard of 'grazing'? This is when everyone just eats bits and pieces when they feel like it, yoghurt here, cheese and crackers there. Sunday nights are often like that in our house—what we call 'one of those dinners'. It's hard to know what overall effect grazing has on nutrition, but it certainly cuts down on communication and probably means no more fights over dinner.

Grabbing a Bite On the Run

As we all know, fast food is a way of life for young people. They rarely have the time to do more than momentarily masticate, let alone gently digest the food they have on the run. It's go, go, go—grabbing a bite is just part of the teenage scene. This wouldn't matter in itself, if take away food were not so rich in fat, salt and energy. Of course, if adults demanded a higher standard, things might change, but for now, we're stuck with what the fast food industry chooses to call 'meeting the community demand'. Most fast foods lack complex carbohydrates, dietary fibre and important nutrients like vitamins A and C. For example:

- An average cheeseburger contains virtually no fibre at all (although the salty fries that often go with it contain a bit)
- The local take away pizza has around 4200 kilojoules (1000 calories) and two grams of salt (approximately four times as much salt as a teenager would need in a day)
- Fried chicken and any meal of fish and chips are loaded with fat

Teenagers love it all and, in reality, few will be adversely affected in any way, particularly those who stay active and make sure that other meals are more nutritious. However, kids should be encouraged to add salad and fruit whenever they can, and not to eat out every day.

Ever noticed how much fluid boys drink? It's amazing, and parents sometimes worry about this too. Gone are the days, of course, when a beverage meant milk or water. Soft drinks and beer have taken over and the consumption figures are mind blowing. While the general population averages just under 70 l of soft drink a year, 14 to 15 year olds do much better. In a 1983 study, Australian girls averaged 148 l and boys a phenomenal 189 l. Work it out—a 375 ml can of soft drink contains nine teaspoons of sugar!

Some teenagers are heavily into vitamins (probably only about 5 per cent or so), in the hope that it might do them some good. The likelihood of real benefit is not strong, in fact, evidence is accumulating about the unfavourable effects of megavitamin therapy. Even more kids are taken in with so called health foods, especially of the sticky (and therefore sugary) kind.

Who's to Blame and What to Do?

Whether or not you are worried and aggravated, or simply bemused and accepting of the way teenagers eat, it is worth wondering why it's the way it is, and what you can do, if anything, to improve matters. First of all, it is clear that teenage eating patterns are influenced by the following factors:

Community Trends

Young people become increasingly aware of what is happening around them. They notice what adults are eating, and adult eating habits have changed significantly (and not for the better) in the past 20 years. According to the respected Australian nutritionist, Rosemary Stanton, virtually every meal has undergone changes, and the 'special foods' once reserved for special occasions only, have become everyday fare. Television and noshing certainly go hand in hand.

Advertisements

The food choices teenagers make are strongly influenced by the way foods are marketed. It works, otherwise manufacturers of processed foods would go broke and that, one supposes, would not be good for the economy. Three interesting points about this:

- A high percentage of all food advertisements are for foods high in fats, sugar or salt

- Many food advertisements are specifically targeted at children and teenagers (those hitting the television screen during prime viewing time, for example)
- The thin young models and actors with clear complexions and gorgeous white teeth seem miraculously immune to the usual effects of the products they are promoting

Pressure from Friends

If teenagers' friends are filling up on foods with little nutritional value, why shouldn't they go along with the fashion? Kids see no problem with this. For one thing, they are living in the here and now. Since many of the ill effects of poor diet take so long to develop (months or years, as a rule), most young people wrongly assume, and convey to each other, that it doesn't matter what they eat.

Parents Themselves

When children turn into teenagers their basic attitudes to eating and drinking are pretty well in place. After all, they've been watching and listening to Mum or Dad for a long time, and these attitudes are not likely to suddenly change. Also, parents still have a major say about what's eaten at home. In fact, the person who does the shopping is the gatekeeper of the family's nutrition (at least the home based part of it). It's certainly difficult to pig out on large quantities of nutritionally empty food at home, if there's none in the house.

While it's important to be realistic, there are a number of things parents can do to help get kids on the right track: by teaching them a few nutritional facts and trying to make nutrition more interesting; by encouraging a varied diet and a reasonably active life; by teaching kids how to cook (thus lessening their reliance on the food industry); by discussing food labels and the sorts of ingredients you seek to do without; by setting an example in your own diet and limiting the number of chocolate biscuits in the cupboard; and finally, by arranging (if possible) a relaxed evening meal. That, at least, will be enjoyable for you too.

Conclusion

A thousand years ago, what people ate was based largely on intuition and what limited foods could be grown, gathered or hunted. The average modern supermarket contains between 8000 and 10 000 items, a dizzying array of mostly processed foods, with highly variable nutritional value and lots of clever, man made chemicals. Children of earlier times had to distinguish between edible and poisonous berries in the bush. Today, the challenge facing kids (all of us really), is to be able to distinguish between nourishing foods and the all too available alternatives.

Adolescents need a balanced, nutritious diet in order to grow, develop and remain healthy. This is an area of their lives that cannot be neglected, and not only because of the shorter term problems. The habits and attitudes they acquire now are likely to endure—and there's the next generation to think of as well.

Recipe for health: Regular exercise plus balanced varied diet

YOUR BODY
Care and maintenance of this instrument shall be the responsibility of the owner

CHAPTER NINE

It's My Body

Ideally, kids should already know a fair bit about their bodies well before adolescence. Parents should see to it. In some schools, the subject of 'how the body works' is presented to eleven-year olds (who don't know at the time how lucky they are), and they love it—it's pertinent, it's timely. Soon enough, if not already, they will have to cope with the myriad of changes we spoke of earlier: a new body shape, newly developed parts and functions, and all the mixed up feelings that go along with puberty.

As well as understanding what the human body is about, children should also be encouraged to value their own as a unique and precious gift, and to look after it as best they can. After all, as the only body they'll get, it has to last them a lifetime. Of course, how one's body looks and how well it functions may not always be within personal control, but how well one cares for it usually is.

Why a chapter on hygiene and fitness? Is there something special about these mundane sounding subjects where young people are concerned? Yes indeed: for adolescents, they are sensitive and important issues (definitely a part of growing pains); for parents, some inspiration is called for. Their brief is to be knowledgable, supportive and influential.

On Being Clean

Parents often find the whole question of a teenager's cleanliness somewhat uncomfortable. It is a bit personal really, but it's one of those things that you can't keep to yourself, at least not indefinitely. For better or worse, if you (or your clothing) are not clean, word gets out.

From a parent's point of view, there's more to this than merely wanting a neat, clean and presentable delegate to the outside world (although that's probably a big part of it). A parent has to live with a teenager too. But there are other and possibly more important considerations as well: how we look and how we feel go hand in hand; hygiene and health are intimately interrelated; and the way we care for and protect our bodies can influence not only the quality, but also the very length of our lives.

A 5 year old child who doesn't know about the dangers of deadly microbes and the importance of handwashing before eating, would be an absolute rarity; a teenager who chooses not to wash would not. The point is, at adolescence, the need to attend to personal hygiene simply becomes more pressing, and parents have to get their message across without driving the poor kid to become an even more lazy or offensive yobbo. The following factors require our understanding:

An Upsurge of Modesty

As you'll recall from Chapter 1, all sorts of interesting and wonderful things are happening to the bodies of young adolescents, and, as is right and proper, they become increasingly disinclined to share these with their parents. An excrutiating shyness may descend upon them.

What Needs to Be Clean?

It depends on your sex. I once put this question to a group of 14 year old secondary school boys when asked to talk about health. I asked them to draw a male body and mark in the parts requiring attention. Apart from a few desultory references to ear wax and belly button fluff, their giggling preoccupation with the genital area clearly indicated where their interests lay. Meanwhile, in the adjoining room, a group of girls were sedately discussing the finer points of menstrual hygiene.

What's the Main Message?

Where values and attitudes are concerned, teenagers will, in due course, take a lead from their parents. But right now, much of their information and beliefs come from the media. Aids to hygiene and grooming for young people are part of a growth industry, and kids are virtually bombarded with messages about it, from medicated soaps for facial spots to sweet smelling after-shave or peppermint mouthwash. Actually, with romance in the air, this 'confident smile and fresh breath' idea probably does hit home. However, they'll do better with toothpaste and floss than with anything they swill.

How Gently Can You Give Bad News?

How do you tell someone you love that they have smelly feet, or bad breath, or body odour? Adolescents often go through a 'disgusting stage', believing people think the worst of them anyway, so why not live up to expectations? A blatant disregard for personal cleanliness can also be a form of rebellion (like messy bedrooms) or an indication of depression. An anonymous gift of toiletries with typed instructions is unlikely to succeed. There is no good alternative to a direct, firm and kindly approach—you care, and it offends you. Just that.

At some stage, in all probability, the game will change. A

teenager may see the light, and suddenly become 'newborn clean'. When that happens, you may as well say goodbye to your bathroom—you may never get in there again!

On Being Fit

The subject of physical fitness is also one that concerns parents, and rightly so. While some parents are going berserk at the side of a football field (quite clearly a form of child abuse), others are pondering the fate of the mooching slouch they live with. In both situations, there are things for parents to know.

Why Be Fit?

The evidence to show that regular exercise is good for you is pretty impressive. It would seem to have everything going for it:

- With effective muscle control comes better posture; with increased physical endurance comes less fatigue
- Physical activity decreases tension and is therefore an effective way of coping with stress and anxiety
- It is claimed that exercise, particularly when it involves a lot of jumping up and down, can actually result in increased height (too late for you)

Regular, moderate exercise has everything going for it

- Exercise contributes to the enjoyment of leisure time (of which, for some kids, there might be a lot later)
- Finally, regular physical exercise helps with weight control and can ward off heart attacks and strokes in later life!

Studies of primary and secondary school children show that their general level of fitness is less than optimal. We're in danger of tarnishing our fitness-oriented, healthy, outdoor-loving image (although the word has already got out that we have one of the highest incidences of heart disease in the world). In fact, in Australia, concern about community fitness at large led to the 'Life Be In It' campaign, the objective being to encourage all Aussies, big and small, to take a greater interest in their health and vigour.

Meanwhile, teenagers are either getting stuck into it, or doing their darnedest to get out of it. For a variety of reasons, a loss of interest in exercise at puberty is not unusual, especially in girls. Possible reasons include: other interests, overweight, under-motivated, not doing well in games at school.

Sporty Teenagers

Having sporty teenagers is fun. There's enjoyment and pride in seeing your kid, bursting with energy and radiant good health, giving it his or her best. You also know that team sports in particular, build self-esteem, comradeship and co-operation. For parents, however, there are a few strings attached.

Without doubt, many parents go out of their way to do the right thing—ferrying kids here, there and everywhere, barracking and supporting at all times of day and in all kinds of weather. I know of one marvellous couple who transported a whole soccer team to the match, week after week, even though their kid was the worst player and rarely got a game. (Apparently they had the biggest car.) Despite their protests at times, teenagers do appreciate the effort and attention.

There are dangers too—the amount of time that sporty teenagers can consume is just part of it. There are other hassles as well, mostly in the form of physical injuries. When these enter your life, it's not only the victim who suffers (although to worry too much about such risks would not be in the spirit of the game).

For a number of reasons, adolescents are vulnerable to injury. In the first place, they are growing at an impressive rate which unsettles the mechanics of the body in a variety of ways: as bones lengthen, the muscles and ligaments spanning the bones and joints get tighter and tighter; as muscles develop, there are imbalances around joints and cartilage becomes particularly susceptible to stress. Some kids have special problems, anatomic malalignments such as knock knees or legs of unequal length.

In addition to these risk factors, there are also errors in technique and errors in training that can predispose kids to trauma. A young overarm bowler, for example, might be in danger of elbow injury or a dancer to knee damage, if their approach is wrong. Perhaps the greatest threat of all, however, is an overzealous or incompetent coach or teacher. For one thing, overtraining is dangerous; the coaching philosophy, 'more is better' may be quite detrimental to the young athlete (particularly during growth spurts).

The possibility of getting hurt obviously depends a lot too on the sport. For example, swimming would involve less chance of accidental injury than soccer. In organised sports, there are two main types of injuries:

- **Acute injuries**—such as sprained ankles, twisted knees (the most common serious injury in most childhood sports) or fractured wrists
- **Overuse injuries**—such as tendonitis (for example 'tennis elbow') or stress fractures of long bones; with the use of systematic, repetitive training to improve fitness or sports skills, in fact, these types of injuries are becoming more common

The important thing is to have sports injuries seen to and treated promptly by doctors or physios with special interest and skill. The field of sports medicine has made major advances in recent years; and enormous amount is now known about the physiology and psychology of childhood sport and the treatment and rehabilitation of sports injuries. Fortunately, there are experts around. One of their main messages is: don't pass off physical discomforts (especially in the lower extremities or back) as growing pains; get it checked out!

The price of success—Secondary school kids say there's no difficulty picking out sporty types—they're the popular ones. It's a highly competitive business actually, especially amongst boys, with young egos depending on success and the admiration that goes with it. There is a problem, of course, when teenagers give their all without any preparation whatsoever. I'm not suggesting that school sporting carnivals should be banned, but it surprises me that there haven't been more deaths. After suddenly competing in several races—the 800 m, the 400 m, and the 100 m sprint—my 14 year old son could hardly move for days. (On other days, he doesn't lift a finger by choice.)

For the serious athlete, however, achieving complete success in a sport takes more than just ability. As one talented young gymnast explains, 'You have to dedicate yourself 100 per cent'. This means making some firm and often extraordinary sacrifices. Teenagers who choose this path know that this maximum effort will only last for a short period of their lives and generally feel that the rewards in the meantime are ample justification.

Pressure to achieve athletically is OK if you can do it, as it is in any other constructive pursuit. But it should go without saying that kids do not fare well when their parents, for their own reasons, or their coach or their school, go overboard. Too much pressure spoils the fun, nothing surer. It can actually tarnish a promising young talent, and that really is a shame. And, let's face it, you can't turn a frog into a prince.

Non-sporty Teenagers

Some people have little or no interest in physical pursuits, and little or no aptitude for them. If this describes your kid, chances are it describes you too—not uncommonly (although not always), athletic propensities are inherited.

Some children are not well co-ordinated at all. Bad luck. If

Not everyone is good at sports... but they can be good at other things

you're unable to hit a ball with a bat, or you're endowed with a talent for falling over your feet, particular sports are simply not for you. Some groups of young people, such as the disabled, have special needs, while really fat kids are in a category of their own. Most team sports are out for a start, and athletics requires a certain litheness and mobile agility that may be lacking. In our sport loving society, the unathletically inclined are likely to be laughed at—not nice, but a fact of life.

Then there's the aesthetic type of kid who'd rather be inside chasing notes up and down a piano than outside chasing a ball up and down a field. What do you do then? You can only lead a horse to water, you say? All is not lost. The generally accepted view is that regular exercise—about half an hour at least, three times a week—should be encouraged. There are many possibilities. For younger teenagers, for example, careering around the neighbourhood on a skateboard or a bicycle, playing table tennis or even indoor bowling are all better than nothing. Getting out to the local swimming pool isn't bad either. Here are some other possibilities that you might suggest:

Lifting weights—not necessarily the best idea for musicians, and it doesn't make kids grow taller (as some may wish), but some

teenagers are suited to it, and with bigger muscles comes greater confidence; it's unlikely to make much of a difference, however, before about 14 years of age and it needs to be properly supervised

Jogging—also has its dangers, but there are definite advantages: unco-ordinated or funny looking kids can jog without shame, at their own pace and either alone or with someone they like (possibly a parent who needs the exercise too); running enables you to see the glorious outdoors and is considered just about the best way to achieve endurance fitness which, unlike mere muscle tone, is a key factor in longer life

Swimming—great for young people who like water, know others who like to swim, have an interest in being with other scantily dressed people (not everybody's shy), and want to get all muscle groups toned up; ironically, with intensive swimming training, there's a somewhat greater chance of overuse injury than soccer training (although with non-sporty kids that's not likely to be a problem)

Aerobics—'episodes of physical activity which exercise the heart, lungs, metabolism and muscles in a context of sociability and enjoyment'; a highly fashionable pursuit and lots of fun, but as with all agility exercises, it's important not to overdo it

There are some non-sporty teenagers, of course, whose athletic skills reside entirely in their finger tips. They prefer to play 'sporty' electronic games on a computer and their achievements can be impressive too. This is what psychologists call 'compensation'. Don't knock it!

Conclusion

Encouraging a child to have a positive regard for his or her body is an important task of parenting, and one that must be administered with tact, sensitivity and love. Simply knowing that hygiene and fitness are integral to a teenager's good health is not enough. Always walking gingerly between interest and intrusion, however, you can achieve a great deal from the side lines. But start early (preferably well before adolescence arrives) because, when the teenage years are in full bloom, you are likely to be told in no uncertain terms, that it is no longer your business.

CHAPTER TEN

The Medical Maze: Illness, Doctors and Hospitals

Not surprisingly, it's taken a long time for teenagers, as a group, to come to the attention of doctors. After all, aren't young people supposed to be the healthiest group in the community? Haven't they survived the chicken pox and made it to the teens with reasonable immunity? And aren't they too young to have the sorts of health problems that beset people of their parents' vintage?

All true. But in many ways, teenagers are seriously underserved by the health system. They often fall through the cracks: too old for paediatricians, too young for adult physicians, and too mistrustful, at times, of the family GP. Consequently, many of their concerns and problems tend to go unnoticed. Also, if adults find it difficult to cope with the medical maze, how much more difficult is it for teenagers? Less naive than small children, but less aware and experienced than adults, they often get the worst deal of all.

For parents, it is not always easy to see the situation through their children's eyes. While kids are young enough to take along to see the doctor, at least you're in a position to advocate. But as they get older, this is certainly not what they want. Even teenagers with a chronic illness, who require ongoing medical care and attention, will want to cope with their own relationships.

OK–so I'm healthy–
but am I NORMAL?

Getting a Good Deal

A doctor once accosted me on a dance floor. He'd heard I was an 'adolescent physician', something entirely new to him. (Perhaps he had visions of a pimply-faced kid playing with a stethoscope.) He said, 'Now look here. What's this adolescent medicine business? Have they discovered some new diseases?'

Well, there actually are a number of conditions that tend to crop up during the teenage years, but as I explained over the blare of the music, that's not the point at all. Doctors have something special to offer young people: by being accessible to them, by knowing what's happening to their bodies and minds, by recognising the intimate relationship between their health and behaviour (which of course is true at any age), and by making every effort to encourage their self-responsibility.

A doctor I admire puts it like this: 'The goal is to assist them to achieve good health, reasonable fitness, emotional stability, and the capacity to cope with challenges and opportunities'.

What a Doctor Should Be

When a teenager visits a new doctor, it probably takes about 3 seconds to 'suss' out what sort of encounter it's going to be. Kids have a sixth sense about it and can accurately read the clues: how the doctor greets you, whether or not you're given an opportunity to talk for yourself, the way questions are put and how the physical examination is conducted.

After all, what's the point of consulting a doctor about something if you don't feel comfortable enough to mention the real reason you came? What's the point of getting an ordinary old check up, if the whole experience leaves you feeling embarrassed and even more worried? Obviously, being treated decently, as an intelligent and reasonable person, is important in any medical encounter at any age. With teenagers, however, there are a number of special considerations.

In an article (in an American medical journal) entitled 'What A Doctor Should Be', 16 year old Jackie Quale offers some important advice to medical practitioners. These are useful insights for parents to have:

- To put it plainly, a doctor should simply be himself or herself. Any put on or false front could destroy a teenager's hope for understanding and help.

Teenagers don't want a doctor to talk, dress or act like a teenager—they already know lots of kids who do that. They want a doctor to be comfortable, friendly and professionally competent.

- Because the teenager is a patient, just like any other, the doctor must always bear in mind his or her right to confidentiality and should encourage discussion of things that might not fall on such a sympathetic ear at home. The doctor must always assume that the patient is an individual. Overreliance on contact with parents tends to destroy much confidence between the doctor and his teenage patient.

Parents can find this change of focus a difficult transition, but it is important to accept it graciously. A doctor who hears the teenager out, whether in your presence or in private, is going to be a valuable resource to your son or daughter. For teenagers, this is part of growing up and assuming self-responsibility.

- It is the listening that proves someone really cares.

Teenagers are wary of adults anyway, so someone who appears busy and distracted is not going to get very far in an interview. It's more the feeling that someone is 'with you', taking an interest in you as a person, than the actual time spent that counts. A doctor who can listen quietly for the hidden, tangential ways in which young people convey their concerns, has something special to offer.

- A doctor can suggest a low starch diet and even prescribe medicine to fight an acne problem. . . , but he or she cannot always understand (or remember) the trauma which accompanies these problems.

The problem itself may not be a threat to life, or even to health, but only an insensitive practitioner would treat an adolescent's bodily (or any other) concerns as trivial. A teenager's 'presenting complaint' represents something important; it gains them entry to the doctor's surgery, and often there's more to it than meets the eye. A 14 year old boy who turns up with a cough or a pain in the chest, for example, could well be enticing the doctor to discover the lump he's noticed under his right breast. How nice to be reassured that it's normal and harmless, and not cancer or the first sign of some abnormal sexual transformation.

- The doctor must not do anything that might be interpreted as offensive to the patient's dignity, and the patient must be kept well covered to avoid unnecessary liberties by the doctor. . . Most of us, I imagine, try to hide our suspicions beneath a calm, collected exterior, but just beneath the surface are these strange thoughts so representative of our minds.

The manner in which a physical examination is performed can leave a lasting impression on a young person. A doctor who respects an adolescent's privacy and modesty, keeps up a running dialogue of reassurance (in comprehensible language), and takes the opportunity to teach kids something about how to care for their bodies, has done more than justice to the whole procedure. A doctor who is perfunctory, rough, or ominously silent (a frown of intense concentration without explanation, obviously means you're dying, right?), does not.

Possibly the most sensitive procedure that a teenage girl can experience is an internal examination. Some girls may want their mothers to be present the first couple of times, others won't.

There's generally a good reason for having one (such as severe menstrual problems or undiagnosed abdominal pain—which could mean an infection such as chlamydia—or because she has become sexually active and needs an annual pap smear). It can be extremely unpleasant, even painful, if it's not approached with gentleness and tact. This means: a quiet explanation of what's to be done, the use of a warmed speculum (there's a special small one for girls whose hymen is intact); and a kindly appreciation that embarrassment is normal.

Teenagers in Hospital

Once again, people have the wrong idea about this supposedly fit and healthy group. Teenagers have accidents, take overdoses, get pregnant and suffer from a variety of serious diseases (such as cystic fibrosis, juvenile rheumatoid arthritis and spina bifida), all of which can require a hospital bed. In fact, if the findings of a survey in Western Australia are anything to go by, approximately one in ten adolescents will have an admission to hospital each year. So we can't pretent it's not important.

For a teenager (or anyone, for that matter), being in hospital is rarely a terrific experience. It's not too difficult to figure out why, but it shouldn't be as awful as it frequently is. On the first occasion, it's just plain scary, as Miss Claire Williams wrote in the *Canteen Newsletter* (published by the Australian Teenage Cancer Patients Society):

> When I first went into hospital I was 13, upset, frightened. Unsure what was going to happen to me. It was as if the impossible had come true. My whole world was shaken up. Upside down.
>
> There were many children playing, laughing, crying. Nurses, rushing about their duties.
>
> Worried faces. Parents. Talking, walking, whispering, hoping, praying. Mother. Thin, flustered, grey hair, weak smile. Comfort. On a bed, a bony, pale child. His dark eyes, innocent, weary. As if this was a normal world. Everyone lived like this.
>
> My bed was standing at attention. In line with all the others—identical, starched, regimental. Faces watching, wondering. White washed walls. The smell of disinfectant.
>
> Greetings. People smiling, warmly, exhaustedly, understandingly. Questions answered, barriers broken. No longer an outsider. I was one of them.

Settling in can be easier said than done. If, on top of illness, pain, and anxiety, a young person is confronted with 'inhospitable circumstances', coping becomes even more difficult. In most hospitals teenagers are put in children's wards or general adult's wards rather than grouped together, which is most unfortunate. At no other time in life is the urge to be with one's age mates more intense. When given the opportunity, teenagers support, teach, reassure and entertain each other. Why not in hospital?

For one thing, hospital staff do not always find teenage patients easy going. They are different, unpredictable. A sick adolescent may be 'reasonable, helpful, cheerful, calm and co-operative at one moment, and depressed, disruptive, demanding, manipulative, obstructionistic, defiant or rejecting of authority at another'. Some nurses actively favour a divide and conquer approach, preferring that they be scattered around. Put them all together and, heaven knows! Noise and mayhem? Graffiti and loud music? Sex and depravity?

The opposite view, as it happens, appears more humane and more valid. There is much research to show that teenagers do not thrive in hospital wards that deprive them of contact with peers, understanding staff, a reasonable timetable, and appropriate activities with which to occupy their time. As young people see it, there are different concerns and problems depending on where they are:

In a **children's ward**, where they are disturbed by younger children and crying babies, teenagers often feel infantilised, resented or ignored, irritated by the small furniture and lack of facilities for teenage gear, embarrassed by a lack of privacy, infuriated by having to turn the television off at a 'ridiculously early hour' (8.30 pm, for example), and dissatisfied with the food (who isn't?)

In an **adult ward**, which is usually more austere and ominous, there are even better chances for the whole experience to be emotionally unsettling. Adolescent patients are psychologically more vulnerable than adults and are really troubled by being in close proximity to the elderly and the dying. In comparison with adult in-patients, they have been shown to have a poorer body image, a greater fear of death and mutilation, greater levels of separation and general anxiety, and much more dissatisfaction with their physical surroundings.

A 14 year old girl with leukaemia experienced these 'adult ward' problems first hand. Her mother, in anguish, wrote to me about it, concluding the letter with these sentiments:

> Regardless of the prognosis, an adolescent's stay in hospital should be conducive to as happy a mental disposition as possible, and not such that the actual medical recovery could be hindered by circumstances such as I have described. I hope that hospital care more suited to the needs of our youth will not be too long forthcoming.

On Being Chronically Ill

Adolescence is a rotten time to have something seriously wrong with your body. Actually, it's not all that uncommon—around one in fifteen young people (possibly more) have 'a significant, medical condition or physical abnormality requiring ongoing care or support' (that is, a chronic disease). For such kids, things can come to a head during the teenage years, growing up can become a much more painful journey. And of course, the whole family is affected.

Let Me Be a Teenager

The parents of ill or disabled teenagers have an awful lot to cope with: they usually feel stressed, guilty, and anxious about the future; marital relationships can suffer; or siblings can feel, and actually be, neglected.

The temptation to overprotect sick kids, to somehow make amends or take on their pain as your own, is almost overwhelming. Unfortunately, this is the absolute opposite of what they need and desire. The obstacles to a healthy adolescence are many and varied, but ironically, the most insurmountable ones are often created by those who mean well and care the most.

What does a chronically ill or disabled teenager want, more than anything else in the world? To be a teenager, to do 'normal' things and to make up his or her mind what to do.

Obstacles to Growing Up

Many aspects of normal adolescence become a greater challenge:

- Not being able to do certain things for yourself, as well as the overprotectiveness mentioned above, may interfere with efforts to grow up and become an individual, reasonably separate from the family. This enforced dependence makes kids very angry, and periodically, they may become unco-operative with their treatment (for example, a diabetic teenager bingeing on cake, or an asthmatic teenager smoking a cigarette between puffs of Ventolin). Doctors call this behaviour 'non-compliance' and it worries everybody concerned, but there's clearly an element of healthy adolescent rebellion in it.
- How you look, and how you think you look (body image), are extremely sensitive matters during adolescence. Any deformity or imperfection, obvious or hidden, real or imagined, can be very troubling to an ill or handicapped young person. For example, having to wear a body brace if you need treatment for curvature of the spine (scoliosis). Sometimes, and with certain disabilities, there may be feelings of disgust, loathing and shame. This has implications in regard to personal hygiene and to an acceptance of one's sexuality (not that the opportunities to express it are likely to be all that great).
- Missing a lot of school or having a condition that rules out certain vocational goals, raises questions about getting a job and eventually becoming economically independent. Of course, a kid with epilepsy can do a lot of things other than becoming an airline pilot or working on towerblocks. A greater problem is to do with community prejudices and a shrinking labour market for young people in general.

Having something wrong with you does not tip the scales in your favour.

- Finally, how are you supposed to end up feeling good about yourself, if the rough and tumble of mixing with friends has been denied you? In some ways, the greatest handicap of all for the disabled young person is loneliness. Problems relating to mobility, transport, and access on the one hand, and shyness, embarrassment and poor self-esteem on the other, keep such kids out of the mainstream of adolescent life, or render their involvement in it awkward and traumatic.

A Question of Attitude

At our clinic we have a poster which features a teenager saying 'What's a girl like me doing with cystic fibrosis? Fighting it!' Some chronically ill teenagers are among the most inspiring people I have known. Under the most trying and adverse personal conditions, with little or no hope for improvement or recovery, they have soldiered on (while healthy people around them often continue whingeing about life's small imperfections). They are (or were), special individuals, carrying their burden with dignity and courage.

Someone I shall call Jane was in this category. As a result of her disease, she was wasted and partially paralysed, but she loved life and made the most of it. Her wry sense of humour and indomitable spirit seemed out of place with her tiny body and difficult circumstances. But she lived each day at a time and managed to work till the day she died.

Why Have Adolescent Services?

We are fortunate to have a comprehensive health system provided by the state which is relatively accessible. I say relatively, because services designed for adults or young children, as most of them are, are often less than ideal for teenagers. Although individual doctors or hospital departments have tried to redress this imbalance there does not appear to be a country-wide policy to help our teenagers.

In Australia they have some services that are medically oriented (such as The Children's Hospital in Sydney) but include the skills of experienced social workers and other youth health workers. Others, like The Second Story in Adelaide, cater primarily to the general social and recreational needs of young people, but have the input of medical staff. It is still very early days for such developments, but at least they've made a start. (The first Adolescent Unit in the world was established at the Boston Children's Medical Centre in 1951 by Dr. J. Roswell Gallagher.)

Like the doctor I mentioned earlier, who was perplexed that there should even be such a field as Adolescent Medicine, others wonder if setting up separate services for this age group is such a good idea. After all, they say, aren't the teenage years merely a part of the continuum of life? Might it not be less divisive to maintain the status quo?

Possibly, but certainly not healthier. The Australian College of Paediatrics has come out very strongly in favour of special services for teenagers, based on the following arguments:

- Teenagers are neither children nor adults and generally do not fit well into existing systems of health care
- Teenagers have special physical and emotional needs and require different types of treatment and care
- Teenagers need and deserve health care providers who are able to relate comfortably to young people
- Teenagers are advantaged, directly and indirectly, by being grouped together (for example, they support each other,

provide a resource for teaching, stimulate clinical research into their needs, and receive better and more comprehensive care)

The wheels, however, move slowly; there are obstacles to change. As Wilfred Trotter once said, 'The mind likes a strange idea as little as the body likes a strange protein and resists it with similar energy'. But there's more to it than that. The subject of adolescent health invariably takes us into the tricky waters of medical politics in hard economic times. For example, whether the diminishing health budget should be spent on preventative care areas such as this, or on high technology interventions like liver transplants.

Conclusion

From time to time for some, more regularly for others, teenagers need doctors and hospitals. They don't always present themselves readily and willingly for care and guidance. It's not easy for young people to confront authoritative oldies (previously known as 'members of the establishment'), especially when they're sick and worried. To a greater extent than adults realise, young people are greatly concerned about confidentiality and privacy and are particularly sensitive to the attitudes of those who care for them.

Parents are not outside this issue. Even though you'll gradually be giving up the reins of control and allowing your kids increasingly to negotiate the health system on their own behalf, your interest in their getting the best possible deal is not going to diminish. You'd, say, be on the look out for doctors having a reputation for being *good with teenagers*. You'd be happy for them to attend special adolescent units with multidisciplinary staff and youth oriented facilities and care. And last but not least, you'd be encouraging to governments putting resources into adolescent health. Our society cannot really afford to do otherwise. As American psychologist, Gerard Kaplan has so aptly put it, 'Cure is costly, prevention is priceless.'

A STATE OF MIND

The confusing double bind bombardment

CHAPTER ELEVEN

Emotional Pressures

Adolescence is stressful. With pressures coming from all directions, inside and out, growing up can feel like negotiating your way through a maze. Unfortunately, many of the signposts and clues that could make this process easier, are kept hidden from view. Teenagers do not always get the help and guidance they need.

The only people who are not stressed at all, are dead. The rest of us have to cope with it as an unavoidable part of everyday life. Likewise, parents cannot create a stress free environment for their kids. On the contrary, simply by being parents, parents are contributing to it. But there is much they can do to lessen the blows.

Stress—The Good and the Bad

Pressure in itself is not the problem. Without it we would get nowhere. If it motivates us and can be controlled, it is clearly a positive force. Particularly when there is an end in sight, pressure can lead to the pride of accomplishment and a boost in morale. In this sense, pressure is a desirable and healthy form of stress.

What is not so good is when pressure is prolonged or cannot be handled. This feels terrible, like you're being throttled or drowning in worries, and gives rise to the symptoms we recognise as stress. This is basically anxiety, and is like being revved up with nowhere to go, a feeling that is familiar to all of us.

A dry mouth, pounding heart, butterflies in the stomach and a sense of impending doom are due to the release of adrenalin. Other discomforts such as headache, backache and abdominal pain result from associated muscle tension. However, feeling dreadful is only part of the problem. Prolonged stress is damaging to the body, either directly or indirectly:

- Blood pressure is increased and fats are released into the bloodstream
- The immune system is suppressed
- There is a greater likelihood of physical illness
- Highly stressed people are also more likely to have 'accidents'

Why Is Adolescence Stressful?

If stress is experienced by everyone from time to time, why should we be particularly concerned about adolescents? The answer is that, as a group, they are generally *more* stressed. Almost 50 per cent of young people report significant stress during the teenage years. The others evidently find it less of a hassle, which is nice to know, and provides a somewhat different image to the one we usually have. However, while adolescence is no longer viewed as a time of continuous, agonising, emotional turmoil, it can be tough.

A Confusing World

Everybody is affected by what is happening in the world. There is so much change and uncertainty, and so much competitiveness, those of us in Western society are living and struggling together in a truly tough culture. The media bring us a constant flow of bad news, of strife and destruction and man's inexorable inhumanity to man. These 'windows on the world', particularly television, do little to create a feeling of inner peace and security.

As young minds come alive to what is going on around them, no wonder they are touched with dismay. Having less to look back upon than adults, young people are greatly concerned with the future. If you were to ask a group of young people whether they thought nuclear war was likely, about half of them would be pessimistic about the future. This is very depressing.

Things are moving too fast. How can teenagers figure out where they fit into the scheme of things, if nothing around them keeps still? There are many ways in which current social trends are making growing up more stressful: the struggle to become a separate individual is complicated by the newer shapes and styles of family life; attitudes to teenage sexuality are characterised by mixed messages and catch 22s; vocational goals are sabotaged by technical advancement and growing unemployment; acquiring a sense of self is confused by changing female-male relationships and roles and muddled community values. Despite all this, kids have to adapt, somehow, to our changing world.

A Time of Internal Conflict

Of course, there's not a lot that parents can do about the information explosion, increasing urbanisation and how the government handles the economy. Of more immediate concern are the individual conflicts that combine to cause stress in teenagers, right before our very eyes.

A basic formula for adolescent stress is the need to reconcile inner drives with outside expectations. This is a balancing act requiring great skill and finesse, for which no young person is fully prepared. In the course of everyday life, for example, a teenager must find a path between personal opinions, peer pressure and parental expectations. Some of the difficulties are as follows:

- The need to express oneself as an individual is in conflict with peer pressure to conform
- The need to compete with one's friends is at odds with the need to win social approval
- The need to achieve independence is complicated by the need for parental support and validation

Little surprise then, that teenagers behave erratically at times. It is impossible to please all the people (including themselves) all the time! Unbeknown to others, they are constantly practising the subtle art of compromise, perhaps without even being aware of it at a conscious level. What will be noticeable to them, of course, is the stress involved.

Remember too, that adolescence is a time of new experiences and new feelings, of strong attachments and bitter losses. It is a time of demands and frustrations. Under normal circumstances, teenagers are stressed by the following: having a rapidly changing body and feeling helpless, the first sexual experience, doing something dangerous or disapproved of, the pressure of exams or other performances, the usual hassles with Mum and Dad, having difficulties with a teacher, not getting along with friends, losing a boyfriend or girlfriend or worrying about the future and what to do.

Who Is at Risk?

Transient upsets and problems are simply part of being an adolescent. As discussed before, emotional ups and downs are to be expected, and it doesn't take much to provoke an attack of either one. Of course, it's not entirely trivial when the cat dies or an exam is failed. Parents are usually able to recognise an acute, discernible stressful experience when they see one, and most would not be so foolish as to underestimate the suffering involved. Empathy and support are indicated, and time usually heals all.

On the other hand, some young people are in a chronically stressful situation, and for that reason are more vulnerable to the adverse effects of stress than their peers. Through having low self-esteem and feeling different and powerless, their experience of internal conflict may become unbearable. Certainly, some resilient individuals cope reasonably well despite the most difficult and trying circumstances, but many don't. These are the kids who are more likely to get into physical, emotional or social difficulty. The following types of teenagers are considered to be at risk:

Kids who are different—a particular burden for adolescents. These include: those suffering from physical or intellectual impairment due to chronic illness or disability; those with an alternative sexuality; teenagers from racial, religious or ethnic minorities (who often find themselves caught between two cultures)

Kids who experience serious losses or other traumas—in particular those related to one's homelife: the experience of losing a parent through death or separation; parental rejection; physical, emotional or sexual abuse; having parents who are alcoholic or suffer from chronic or mental illness

Kids in difficult external circumstances—often for reasons beyond their control (including most of the above): kids who are homeless, unemployed, very poor; those in institutional care or living in remote areas

Emotional Problems

Clearly, the experience of stress is a natural part of growing up. However, if the stressors are overwhelming or not dealt with in a healthy way, they can lead to emotional and physical disorders with potentially serious consequences.

When is the situation more serious? Twelve to 15 per cent of adolescents (even more in urban areas) are believed to have a significant psychiatric disorder. The clues are to be found in the young person's mood and behaviour.

Suicide—A One Way Ticket

There is justified community alarm at the rising suicide rate and increasing suicidal behaviour among young people. It is becoming a major social problem. The incidence of suicide in young men has tripled during the past two decades, such that it is now second only to road accidents as the major cause of teenage deaths. The suicide rate for girls has remained relatively stable.

DEPRESSION
CONCERN
ONE-WAY TICKETS
INTERVENTION
FOR ASSISTANCE GRASP HAND
ANGUISH
UNRELIEVED SADNESS
EXCESSIVE TIREDNESS
DETERIORATING SCHOOLWORK
MOOD CHANGES

Of course, many more young people make an attempt on their lives than actually succeed.

Although more girls than boys try to kill themselves, boys are more likely to use an effective method (such as hanging or shooting themselves), which is why they succeed more often. A girl might take an overdose of pills (tranquillizers, for example) or put a cut in her wrists, and make sure someone knows about it pretty soon afterwards. Tragically, some teenagers who make half hearted attempts end up losing their lives anyway. Studies seem to indicate that adolescent suicides for girls occur far more in the inner, less affluent suburbs, while for boys occur more often in the wealthier suburbs.

The media are quick to point the finger at such factors as family breakdown, unemployment and homelessness, while psychiatrists believe that uncritical media reporting itself may actually be contributing to the trend. Young people may be getting brainwashed into believing that there is no future worth living for, an insidious and sinister process that should be of great concern to us all. There are three ways in which adolescent suicides can occur:

- A young person takes his or (less commonly) her life through a deliberate and obvious suicidal act
- In some cases, an accidental death (say in a car or motorcycle accident) is actually a 'disguised suicide' in a depressed teenager
- Suicide can occur indirectly when young people choose to take drugs or live a lifestyle deliberately chosen to slowly kill themselves

This subject is complex and distressing and, not surprisingly, many people view it as something that is happening 'out there'. But a lot of lives are touched by it. In a poignant press article, a mother whose daughter had committed suicide made this plea:

> If you are a teenager reading this, don't give up on life. Death is a one way ticket, marked 'not negotiable'. That body in the morgue is no longer yours to make choices with. Suicide is a game where everybody loses—your parents, your friends and most of all you.

How Can You Tell When a Teenager Is Depressed?

Of course, with suicide, the focus is on the end point, but there is a process involved. Reaching a point of desperation does not occur overnight. What underlies increasing suicidal behaviour is an awful lot of adolescent depression and only recently has this been widely accepted as existing.

Although there are similarities between the depressive illness suffered by young people and adults, there are also major differences. It's not always easy to tell, but teenagers generally reveal their depression in three ways: sadness, physical symptoms or antisocial behaviour:

Depressed kids are usually **sad and downhearted** and don't bounce back as you would normally expect. There is nothing unusual about sporadic tearful, sullen and irritable behaviour, but when this goes on and on, it suggests that something is amiss. There are also some indirect signs: they're not interested in activities they used to enjoy; they become apathetic and have trouble concentrating; deteriorating schoolwork is a dead giveaway and sometimes there is a distancing from family and friends. When parents start to feel 'I don't know you anymore' and sad vibes are coming through most of the time, there's likely to be more to it than an ordinary bout of the 'downs'.

Depressed kids are often **physically unwell** and may complain of frequent headache, other aches and pains or the general 'blahs' (to be discussed further in the next section). Excessive tiredness is also very common, and researchers have shown that depressed young people tend to sleep longer than healthy individuals (and awake less fatigued, suggesting that the extra sleep may actually be helping them in some way). Remember too, that viral infections such as glandular fever (infectious mononucleosis) can leave you feeling fatigued and depressed, sometimes for months.

Depressed kids may also show **uncharacteristic behaviour**—that is, behaviour that is unusual for them—which can mislead people into thinking anything but the truth. (See the discussion on Acting Out on page 181.) In this situation, the depression is said to be 'masked', although the sadness will be evident if looked for. Meanwhile, depressed kids who are hyperactive, disruptive, aggressive or frankly antisocial (for example stealing), frequently become young offenders. Punishment at the hands of the authorities (school, welfare or the law) becomes their treatment, which is hardly appropriate!

Very depressed teenagers have morbid thoughts, feelings of anguish, loss and hopelessness and a mounting sense of frustration and alarm. This is an unbearably painful state and the idea of escape through suicide becomes very appealing (which brings us back to where we started). Hopefully, before this advanced stage is reached, someone will have tuned into what is going on, a professional opinion sought and the appropriate counselling provided. It is literally a matter of life and death.

Why Do Teenagers Get Depressed?

The overriding themes in adolescent depression are loss and bereavement. Kids who belong to the groups listed above have more than enough reason to be depressed. Let's face it, if parents die or leave or become seriously ill, or if they are abusing or always drunk or constantly fighting, it would be abnormal *not* to be depressed.

Less obvious, but equally important, is parental behaviour that destroys a young person's self-esteem. This can involve excessively high and inappropriate expectations or, alternatively, behaviour that is constantly critical or disparaging. Rejection can take many subtle forms and its effects are serious.

Although no age group is immune, it is important to realise that older teenagers are at greater risk. This is because they generally have more emotional investment in people and things. For example, a relationship that breaks down can be quite devastating at 18 or 19 and would often lead to depression, whereas a 14 or 15 year old kid, buffered by the peer group, would be more likely to just roll with it. Also, in the late teens and early twenties, a young person is less inclined to reach out to the family for support—the need to be grownup and independent gets in the way.

Rejection can take many subtle forms

Is This Kid Really Sick?

In one survey carried out in the late seventies, over half of the young people (in the 12 to 18 age group) reported that they had felt significantly unwell in the previous fortnight. And this is supposed to be the healthiest time of life? As a group, teenagers experience a lot of physical symptoms, some of which, no doubt, are merely growing pains. Others are more serious and debilitating and interfere with their (and their family's) enjoyment of life.

Psychological stress has been implicated as a contributory factor in virtually all diseases, but that is another problem. Many sick young people, perhaps the majority, do not have a physical illness. Their malady is stress related, what health professionals now prefer to call *abnormal illness behaviour* (AIB), rather than the hackneyed and confusing term, psychosomatic disorder.

The physical symptoms of AIB can be literally anything, but commonly include aches and pains (headache and abdominal pain are the most common), lethargy or vague feelings of ill health. Of course, a doctor will be able to rule out such things as glandular fever, infectious hepatitis or withdrawal from too much coffee. In their absence, AIB should be suspected when the symptoms have the following characteristics:

- They are overvalued, that is, there is a preoccupation with their importance beyond what one would expect (for example, a teenager with headaches but otherwise well, who finds it hard to think about anything else)
- They are out of proportion to the physical findings (that is, a doctor can find no adequate evidence to account for the degree of discomfort or disability)
- They are enduring and distressing, and not merely minor or occasional complaints (like a momentary twinge)

In such cases, a frustrating medical merry go round in the search for a respectable disease will not provide the answer. The challenge is to understand what the illness means. Why does this adolescent need to behave sickly and why now? Psychiatrists view abnormal illness behaviour as some sort of adaptation to a real or imagined threat, often related to past or present distress within the family (such as bereavement, parental illness or an unhappy marriage). Unfortunately, as a way of dealing with a difficult or troubling situation, it doesn't do the adolescent any good at all.

As none of this is happening at a conscious level, it takes a bit of sorting out. For that reason, when a teenager persists in being unwell, the help of the whole family may be enlisted. An inter-

Is this kid really sick?

view involving whoever lives at home (Mum, Dad, brothers and sisters, perhaps even Grandma) can often lead to a better understanding of the situation. It is never a matter of seeking to blame someone. The goal of treatment is to find a more healthy way for the family to cope so that the young person can get back to normal and get on with the job of growing up.

A Boy Called John

The family of a boy I'll call John illustrates how things can work out when this approach is taken. John was a 13 year old boy who had been sick for many weeks with a sore throat, abdominal pain, headaches and vomiting. Both his parents were very keen to find a physical cause for his symptoms (which had also occurred a number of times before), but many medical tests and consultations had failed to reveal one.

During the course of several family interviews with a doctor and a social worker, the following information emerged:

- Father, a business executive, had recently changed his job (having lost his previous one) and this had led to significant marital tension
- Mother, who also worked, suffered from frequent migraines and excessive tiredness (another instance in the family of medical symptoms reflecting stress)

- The children—John, his older sister and two younger sisters—griped a lot initially about household chores (particularly when things got tense between Mum and Dad). Eventually, they were able to express their fears that their parents might separate. Although John was the one presenting with an illness, they all had strong fantasies of being deserted by either their mother or their father.

The main outcomes of these preliminary family meetings were that John's symptoms rapidly became less overvalued and then settled, and the parents sought further help for themselves.

Acting Out—Another Sort of Cry for Help

Most adults are intolerant of adolescent behaviour that is irrational, aggressive or anti-social, and who can blame them? This is pretty threatening and we do hear a lot about it, particularly the 'crisis mentality' that has us believing that adolescents (or youths) are basically rotten.

As a rule of thumb, it is often helpful to remember that most (probably all) behaviour has meaning. The challenge is to understand it. A lot of 'difficult' adolescent behaviour can be understood in terms of certain needs. For example, young people need:

- To be 'on the go'. As we discussed in Chapter 2, action and activity help kids to get rid of pent up energy, as well as dealing with anxiety, escaping from trouble by riding off into the wild blue yonder, etc. (Did it ever occur to you that the humble bicycle served such a therapeutic role?)
- To test the limits of control. This goes on throughout childhood and requires a structure within which kids are free to experiment. Without clear limits, the testing may go outside the family and become of interest to the law! For example, a teenager from a very permissive home might get involved in acts of vandalism as a means of inviting some sort of restrictions

'Acting out' is different. This means that a person does something in order to avoid experiencing painful feelings. In a sense, thought is replaced by action, and the internal conflict is brought out into the open. It is acted upon, even though the action may not obviously relate to the feeling inside. For example, a teenager may be feeling very sad because his parents have separated, but instead of being able to articulate this feeling to others (let alone to himself), he may go out drinking or stay out all night.

One of the consequences of acting out is that the individual feels better (for example, less sad), without understanding what the behaviour means. But in so doing, the underlying feelings that cannot be directly faced and dealt with, remain hidden. For this reason acting out must be viewed as a cry for help.

Acting out can take different forms as Newcastle psychologist, Frøydis Boulton, points out:

Occasional acting out—The behaviour seems unusual or out of character and is occurring in response to a specific circumstance or situation. The acting out may be an alternative to say, feeling sad (as above) or guilty. Teenagers can feel guilty struggling against parents who are resisting their efforts to grow up—they may want to do what is expected of them but can't. For example, a teenager might not be allowed out at night or to spend time with his or her friends. Sneaking out through the window after one's parents are asleep (to go to a special party perhaps), could qualify as acting out. Interestingly, guilt-laden adolescents sometimes commit a blatant delinquent act, such as stealing something, in order to be punished, after which they often feel greatly relieved without knowing why.

Acting out

Habitual acting out—This is the so called 'impulse ridden adolescent' who acts out virtually all the time. They are thrill seekers, who drive like maniacs and revel in danger and violence. Unaware of the underlying reasons for their behaviour, they are constantly in strife. Such teenagers have usually had a really rough time in infancy and childhood. Deprived of adequate care and affection in early life, they have difficulty getting close to people, and view the world and its inhabitants with suspicion and anger.

Acting out in search of the past—Some young people sense that something is missing from their lives. Crucial past events are either unknown or have been kept hidden, and the acting out represents a strange attempt at remembering. Foster children and children adopted late often fall into this category, but sometimes parents have kept a secret, ostensibly to protect the child, but more often to protect themselves. One troubled boy in all sorts of strife was actually the illegitimate son of the young woman (now married) he thought was his older sister.

Acting out on behalf of parents—The verbal instruction from the parent might be, 'Don't do it' (don't get pregnant, don't drive recklessly), but the 'twinkle in the eye' or the excessive interest in a detailed account of what subsequently happens provides a different message. In other words, the expected outcome seems different from the spoken statement, and teenagers readily pick up a covert nod to go ahead. In effect, there is a self-fulfilling prophecy to do with the needs of the parent. Of course, the 'forbidden' behaviour provokes much fuss and punishment, while the vicarious thrills and excitement are covered up. As with the other types of acting out, the underlying reasons are not experienced at a conscious level.

In practice, things would probably not be quite this clear cut. Maybe the kid really is just plain rotten, but generally it is more helpful to try to see 'bad' behaviour in context. Sometimes, as with severe emotional damage in early childhood, little can be done. In other circumstances, a troubled teenager can be helped by individual or family counselling. Sometimes, residential treatment would be ideal, but suitable facilities (that is, those offering a structured environment for acting out adolescents) are few and far between. Overall, the outlook will usually be better if parents do not distance themselves too far from what is happening. After all, whether or not parents are part of the problem, they need to be part of the solution.

Just a Little Crazy

The feeling that everybody's just a little crazy (apart from you and me) is pretty normal. Of course, really strange people generally don't know that they're strange, and would a friend tell them? Actually, that's part of the problem. Odd characters tend not to have many friends.

The loner, for example, is easy to pick. The young person who shuns friends and remains aloof, isolated and seemingly self-contained is said to have a withdrawn (or schizoid) personality. Chances are that such kids are basically OK and will simply grow up to become fairly withdrawn and isolated adults. But in later adolescence, when stresses tend to build up, there is a possibility of becoming more seriously disturbed (also for the reasons discussed in the section on depression).

On the other hand, some teenagers are unable to develop a mature identity and become lost in endless self-questioning and soul searching (so called 'identity disorder'). Despite intellectual or other abilities, such individuals fail to fulfill their potential, feel like misfits, despair of ever forming worthwhile relationships and frequently drop out of the mainstream.

Serious Psychiatric Disorders

The 'schizophrenic' who said 'I'm crazy and so am I' clearly didn't understand the nature of the problem. Contrary to the popular stereotype, schizophrenia has nothing to do with split personality but definitely is a serious and mostly life long psychiatric disorder.

Schizophrenia is characterised by deteriorating school performance, withdrawal, inappropriate responses to people (such as laughing inanely when nothing funny has happened), an inability to think normally, imagined happenings or voices, feelings of persecution, and at times markedly childish behaviour. It may come on acutely or insidiously and may occur any time after the age of 7 years, but tends to increase in incidence between the years of 15 to 20. Before adulthood, for reasons that are not understood, the condition is three times as common in males, but thereafter, the sexes are equal. The cause of schizophrenia is unknown, although there are probably many factors involved (genetic, biochemical, communication, family functioning etc).

Other psychiatric disorders occur in adolescence and are also mercifully rare. Needless to say, if a young person becomes totally manic and buys the Harbour Bridge or takes to washing his or her feet a hundred times a day, you will know who to call. In fact, whenever serious emotional problems are suspected, seek professional advice. They are unlikely to just go away of their own accord.

What Parents Can Do About Emotional Pressures

Researchers are keen to know, given similar circumstances, why adolescence is plain sailing for some and so terrible for others. They look closely at childhood experiences and what's happening in families, for in these settings of time and place the clues must lie. (In a recent Canadian study, the health concerns and habits of over 700 young people aged between 12 and 20 were examined. Not surprisingly, in relation to emotional and social problems, difficulties at school and at home were the most important.) Of course, where there are problems, there are also potential solutions.

How Can We Help Kids Handle Stress Better?

Adults have become very interested in the idea of stress management, but obviously, the earlier such skills are learned, the better. It is generally accepted that:

- People with strong support systems live longer and suffer less stress related disease than those who feel isolated and lonely
- Certain lifestyle habits are helpful in strengthening us against the effects of stress: a sensible diet, adequate sleep and regular exercise; an ability to 'slow down', do one thing at a time and achieve a reasonable balance between work, rest and play

Parents can set the scene throughout childhood. They can encourage kids to view pressure as a challenge, to cope with hard knocks courageously and well, and to develop skills for dealing with the more serious threats to their emotional equilibrium. Much has been written on this subject, but the keys are rehearsal, relaxation, 'self talk' and assertiveness:

Rehearsal—It is extremely important that children are able to anticipate stressful or dicey situations they might encounter and mentally 'practise' possible solutions. (This is obviously relevant to 'risk taking' to be discussed in the next chapter.) For example, a teenager might decide to avoid being exposed to something stressful (such as unprotected sexual intercourse) or be prepared to take some sort of positive action (such as talking things through, soon, with someone he or she trusts). Parents can help simply by talking openly with kids about their concerns and ideas in such matters.

Talking things through

Relaxation—a potent antidote to stress and a major advantage to a young person facing, say, an exam or a public performance (such as giving a speech or having an interview for a job). Since transcendental meditation was introduced to the West in the early 1960s, millions of devotees throughout the world have taken it up in order to achieve 'a state of conscious restfulness' (usually for about 20 minutes twice a day). Teenagers might not be too taken with this approach, but it will be useful to them to know how to get calm quickly. They can easily learn the following technique:

- Take several slow, deep breaths, relaxing the shoulders while breathing out; then allow breathing to become quieter and more peaceful
- Relax the muscles of the face and jaw; once a person's facial expression becomes tranquil and at ease, the mind and body tend to follow.

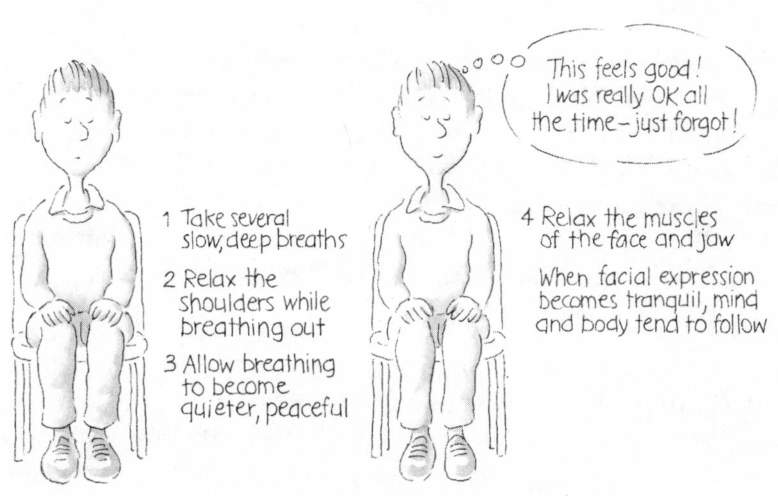

'Self talk'—of a positive kind! When things go wrong, most people put themselves down ('I probably deserved it, anyway'); positive 'self talk' is the opposite, a magic mental tool for building up self-esteem in the face of adversity ('Well, I tried my best in the ballet exam. Next time will be better.') Kids need to be actively encouraged to be kind to themselves. They should be reminded, for example:

- That every person is unique and of value—so think often about all your good points
- That positive thoughts absorb anxiety—so focus on the good things you are looking forward to in the future
- That people with a sense of humour handle stress better (smiling reduces tension and makes you more likeable)—so reach out and make contact.

Assertiveness—probably the most important anti-stress attribute one could possibly acquire, and one we tend to underestimate. Assertiveness simply means saying and doing what is right for you (without being aggressive or threatening) in situations where there is pressure to do otherwise; assertiveness is about communicating effectively in situations of stress—and if that means saying 'NO' (the most important assertiveness tool of all), then that's what you say.

The take home message for parents seems to be, therefore, teach your children: to think about what's likely to be upsetting to them, to talk about it at any stage (both to themselves and to others), and to take positive action in their own interests, as mentioned above.

When Outside Help Is Needed

Some people are natural, receptive, supportive listeners. They have an instinct for what is required in a given situation and don't fall apart in a crisis. Kids who have access to someone (perhaps a favourite aunt or school teacher) who answers this description are fortunate indeed. It is very reassuring for a troubled teenager to be able to 'talk things through' with an empathic, extra-parental adult, even one who 'calls a spade a spade'.

Sometimes, however, the special skills of a trained counsellor are needed. In expert hands: pent up feelings can be let out; problems evaluated; solutions explored; and resources engaged. Good counselling is a collaborative venture in which the recipient is encouraged to capitalise on strengths, to face realities and make choices, to find a direction to go in.

To reiterate the major danger signals:

- Frequent or prolonged mood disturbance (including being too up or too down)
- Deteriorating school marks and the inability to perform at previous levels
- Sexual behaviour involving exploitation, anxiety and guilt
- Repeated acts of anti-social or self-destructive behaviour

Conclusion

Emotional pressures are a fact of life, while you're growing up and forever more. Certainly, it's important to learn how to cope with them, and not to let them grind you down. But there's more to success and happiness than merely coping with stress. There's optimism.

An optimist has been described as 'someone who tells you to cheer up when things are going his way'. Don't believe it. Optimists know what they want and go after it. Australian entrepreneur Michael Edgley has put it well. In an address given at the National Youth Forum in 1979, he made the following illuminating point:

> Successful people are supreme optimists. They get enthusiastic about their own dreams, they then tend to turn that optimism into action. You will notice that in their vocabulary they have words like 'I want to', 'I can', 'I will'.

Ideally, we should start giving our kids this sort of message before they are even born. But it's never too late!

3
3
ROAR!!

CHAPTER TWELVE

Taking Risks

Life is a risky business. We all take chances, and there are risks involved in practically everything we do. Taking risks is certainly a natural part of growing up. Teenagers have a special thirst for new experiences. They are eager to try out new skills, to test the limits of their abilities, to compete, to challenge, to rebel.

In the course of their exuberant experimentation, however, young people put themselves at risk of physical damage, or worse. It is normal for parents to worry about this, but preferable for them not to panic. You may already be doing all the right things. This chapter looks at what risk taking is about and discusses those 'health hazardous behaviours' that cause parents so much anxiety and anguish.

Why Do Teenagers Take Risks?

Young people are by nature experimental. How else can they work out what is not safe, sensible and right for them? Only the most timid and fearful of parents would want a teenager to be a motionless blob who never takes chances—the outcome would be not to grow up. Obviously, there's more to it than this. Multiple factors influence adolescent risk taking, including those related to the individual, relationships with others, and the outside world.

At a **personal level**, all adolescents are curious about what life has to offer. Some behaviour is just 'to see what it's like'! Remember too, that those in the frenzied grip of pubertal hormones and bursting at the seams with energy tend to be impulsive. Kids often do things on the spur of the moment, with little thought for the consequences. In fact, immature or changing thinking processes may interfere with the actual perception of risk, giving the false impression of a *laissez faire* attitude.

For a minority of teenagers, however, dangerous behaviour is motivated by psychological factors (as discussed in the previous chapter): stressed kids are more likely to have accidents; taking risks may offer them a means of escape from feelings and conflicts that are too painful to face (acting out); or there may be underlying suicidal wishes. Sometimes, risk taking is to do with a lack of satisfaction in other things. If you're in rotten circumstances (homeless and unemployed, for example), perhaps getting high is the best thing going.

At a **relationship level**, most teenagers are pretty involved with other people, so what they do is not purely and simply a matter of individual choice. It is happening within the context of families and friends, each having a strong influence on a young person's beliefs, behaviour and approaches to life. These influences contribute to a teenager's lifestyle which has both immediate and long term effects on his or her health and wellbeing.

Much adolescent behaviour appears designed to impress one's friends, or at least to win their approval. The need to be 'one of the group' is a powerful motivation to behave in certain ways, to the extent that peer pressure sometimes achieves pride of place as a parent's number one concern (not entirely unreasonable). But before getting out the shotgun, consider this. In seeking adult status (what growing up is all about, for goodness' sake), young people are drawn to what they perceive as 'adult activities'. They want to do what the grownups are doing, and who are they watching the closest?

Yes. Parents may inadvertently contribute to the risk taking behaviour of teenagers in at least four ways:

- By the behaviour they 'model', for example, a teenager is twice as likely to smoke if both parents smoke
- By the behaviour they disapprove of, especially when it comes in a stern, 'it's bad for you and you must not do it' tone of voice, thus giving kids something to rebel against

- By the behaviour they 'set up', through subtle messages and vicarious enjoyment, as in 'my big, strong son the tough athlete'
- By behaviour they avoid, for example not setting appropriate limits for their teenager as in, 'It's your life, do what you want!'

And finally, at the broader **societal level**, there are influences beyond personal and family control. Naturally, life would be a lot safer for young people if gigantic motorcycles, hotted up cars and dangerous substances did not exist at all. But they do. What's more, the current human condition and adult self-interest conspire to encourage their use.

On the one hand, there are the depressing realities of troubled and confused families, unemployment and the nuclear threat (giving rise to an understandable 'what the hell?' attitude). On the other hand, there is media bombardment with sexual innuendoes, the general glorification of violence (life in the fast lane), and the commercial exploitation of the young through alcohol and tobacco advertising (a package thoroughly deserving of the label, 'ill health promotion'!).

Media bombardment

What Risks Do Teenagers Take?

Risk taking can take a variety of forms, ranging from not getting enough sleep and eating the wrong food, to behaviour that constitutes a more serious threat to health and life. Chapter 3 looked at sexual risk taking (unprotected intercourse when a pregnancy would be unwelcome; exposure to STDs). This section discusses accidents, alcohol, tobacco and (last but not least) other substances of abuse.

Teenagers and 'Accidents'

Where adolescents are concerned, accidents take on a somewhat different meaning. The usual implications of 'random and inevitable happenings' don't quite fit, when there is a multitude of contributing factors. 'Traumatic events' or 'non-intentional injuries' would be more appropriate terms.

Road crashes take more young lives than any other single cause, so it is fitting to consider these first:

- Young males are involved in more road accidents than young females
- A large number of road accident deaths are in the 16 to 20 year age group and, of these, many injuries are sustained as a result of motor cycle crashes
- More than half of the alcohol related accidents resulting in injury or death on the road involve young people between the ages of 16 and 24
- A substantial proportion of the 16 to 20 year old riders or drivers involved in serious accidents have a recordable blood alcohol level: mostly young men, but also a significant number of young women aged 16 to 25, who have accidents, drive under the influence of alcohol or are passengers in cars driven by people under the influence

Sitting behind the wheel of a car and burning along at breakneck speed is an exhilarating experience for a teenager. The question is, who's in control—the kid or the car? As a breed,

young drivers tend to be impulsive, careless, distractible, and just a touch immortal (sounds a bit like some 'adult' drivers). Not infrequently, it seems, they are also intoxicated! Even a blood alcohol level of 0.05 doubles the crash risk; at 0.15, a crash is twenty-five times more likely.

In our highly motorised society, getting a driver's licence is a rite of passage equal to none. Practically all 16 year old kids want this desperately. The dilemma seems to be that teenagers are learning to drive at the same time as they're learning to drink! We are yet to discover a satisfactory answer to this. Legislation relating to minimum drinking and driving ages, seat belts and helmets take us only part of the way.

While fatal accidents are mainly connected with traffic, non-fatal accidents more commonly occur during sport or in the work place. Young people are particularly at risk in industry, where their lack of preparation, experience and care often make a traumatic combination. Workers between the ages of 15 and 24 have the highest rate of work accidents and it appears, from compensation figures over the past 10 years, that these rates are increasing.

Teenagers and Alcohol

As part of the government's national drug offensive (the effectiveness of which is yet to be evaluated), youth oriented media, such as radio, television and magazines, are being used to send the message to teenagers that even if they *think* they've got it under control, they haven't. Huge grim-looking posters on public hoardings reinforce this message. Hard hitting stuff, and in terms of more recent statistics, pretty pertinent.

Teenagers drink about twice as much as they did 15 years ago. In Australia they have been watching the drug taking behaviour of New South Wales school students aged 12 to 17 years closely since 1971. The 1983 figures in regard to alcohol use reveal the following:

- Boys and girls now have very similar rates of alcohol consumption, even at 14. The girls have caught up, reflecting the fact that the stigma attached to female drinking has all but disappeared in Australia
- Heaviest adolescent drinking occurs amongst 16 and 17 year olds (almost 15 per cent of whom are drinking alcohol on a daily basis); half of this age group reported knocking back five or more drinks in a row in the previous fortnight
- By the age of 17, boys are conforming to the macho image and drinking mostly beer, while girls prefer the sophistication of Smirnoff or Bacardi and Coke (let's hear it for advertising)—sweet drinks that don't taste like booze but write you off
- On the other hand, over 90 per cent of 12 and 13 year olds hardly drink at all (well, less than one drink a week, anyway)

A generation of young people is starting to drink in the teens. They start with the idea that you can only relax socially if you have a drink. (Wherever did they get that idea?) According to a recent survey, in comparison to teenagers in the United States and New Guinea, Australian kids are much more likely to report that both parents drink, and are more likely to have been offered their first drink by parents or relatives.

We shouldn't be too surprised. We're the country that downs more alcohol than any other in the Western world—an average of 9.7 l of absolute alcohol per head of population per year. (This means 2.6 standard drinks per head per day, and obviously some people don't drink at all.) Over the past 10 years, the consumption of table wines has increased by 150 per cent. What's depressing about all this is that alcohol related illness is a major health problem, following on the heels of heart disease, cancer and mental illness.

The acute problems are bad enough: drunkenness, violence, arrests and accidents. Alcohol is a depressant (not a stimulant as many people think) and is dangerously intoxicating, especially to young people who don't yet know how much they can handle. Teenage deaths from toxic overdose have usually involved a dare to down a bottle of spirits. For most young drinkers, however, dangerous behaviour and drunk/drugged driving pose a greater threat to life.

Longer term problems are less obvious. While no one can say for sure whether or not teenage drinking patterns persist into adulthood, the earlier you start, and the heavier you drink, the earlier you get damaged. The details are depressing: cirrhosis of the liver, some cancers, chronic malnutrition and the risk of infection, and of course, brain damage. Yes, heavy drinkers get a shrinking brain—an absolute loss of cortical tissue (reversible, fortunately, in young people who stop before it's too late).

Parents won't have too much trouble noticing when a teenager staggers home looking green around the gills or wakes up with a hangover. But there are some other early warning signs that might suggest that drinking is getting out of hand, for example: increased moodiness and aggressiveness, shaky hands, sleeplessness and anxiety and deteriorating school or work performance (none of which, of course, are exclusive to alcohol abuse).

Parents who are worried about their teenagers' drinking can get advice from their local Community Health Centre (who may even employ specialist drug and alcohol workers), or call a 24 hour drug and alcohol information service (which is usually located at a hospital). In cases of acute intoxication, the best thing to do is call a doctor or an ambulance.

Teenagers and Smoking

We have been told, albeit quietly, that tobacco is the biggest, single killer. Thirty per cent of all fatal cancers could be prevented by people not smoking. The smoking habit gains an insidious hold on the smoker who then finds it very difficult or impossible to give it up. Teenagers should be told this.

Community attitudes to smoking are slowly changing. 'Passive smoking', for example, is of greater concern than it was several years ago. It is now known that children are getting hefty doses of nicotine, simply by living in a household with a smoker—the equivalent of eighty cigarettes a year in fact, if both parents smoke. In more public places, smoking is now prohibited.

To reiterate a couple of points made earlier:

- The influence of close friends who smoke is the number one reason for starting
- A teenager is twice as likely to smoke if both parents smoke, and four times as likely to smoke if parents and older siblings smoke

Fortunately, however, the majority of adolescents do not smoke. Amongst those who are smoking (less than a third of 15 to 19 year olds), most smoke irregularly or less than five cigarettes a day (in contrast to an adult smoker who averages almost a packet a day). During the secondary school years, however, daily smoking increases with age and, by 17, twice as many girls as boys are smoking each day. While more boys are quitting or not starting, girls are increasingly taking it up, hence the reversal in male-female ratios.

No doubt, many factors account for this disturbing trend but, despite blustering denials by cigarette advertisers, a link is cleverly drawn for young women between smoking and sexual attractiveness. It seems to be working. A lot of girls smoke in the belief that it will prevent them from getting fat (part of the same message). Some special concerns for young women are worth emphasising:

- Teenagers who become pregnant and continue to smoke are endangering the health of their unborn babies (through the increased risk of stillbirth, prematurity and abnormally low birth weight)
- Breast fed babies of smoking mothers may have nausea, vomiting, diarrhoea and a rapid heart rate
- Compared to the children of non-smokers, children of mothers who smoke have twice as many colds, are sick more often and take longer to recover from illnesses

Nobody should need any convincing that teenage smoking is a major health problem. The longer term consequences in particular (a fifteen times greater chance of developing lung disease and lung cancer and an eight times greater chance of heart disease) are being well publicised. However, teenagers who smoke soon develop a cough, produce phlegm and become short of breath on exertion, lose stamina, get a bad taste in the mouth, stains on their teeth and an unpleasant odour on their breath, fingers, hair and clothes. Smoke also irritates eyes and causes skin to wrinkle faster.

What people don't seem to realise is that nicotine is an extremely addictive drug. Recent research suggests that kids can get hooked pretty quickly (perhaps after less than one pack) and actually need to continue smoking. However, it's encouraging to know that, if a young person under 25 is able to stop smoking, the health risks revert to normal. It takes 7 to 10 days to be free from nicotine, and the cough, wheezing and mucous start to improve in 2 to 3 weeks. For teenagers who want to stop, as one would hope they will, all kinds of help is readily available.

Teenagers and Other Drugs

Despite all the statistics and known dangers concerning alcohol and tobacco, other drugs really worry parents the most. Of all these, marijuana is undoubtedly the most popular. By contrast, other illegal drugs which include hallucinogens (LSD), amphetamines (speed), narcotics (heroin), cocaine (and its cheap, fast acting and extremely addictive derivative, 'crack') are used by relatively few young people. In a study of 2000 college students in Sydney, aged 15 to 19, 12 per cent of boys and half as many girls had used these drugs in the previous month.

Where secondary school students are concerned, three categories of drug usage are worthy of comment: solvent and aerosol sniffing; analgesics and tranquillizers; and marijuana.

Solvent and aerosol sniffing has become a popular form of drug experimentation. The substances used include glue, petrol, lighter fluid, cleaning fluid, paint thinner, etc. About 50 per cent of students throughout the secondary school system admit to trying it. Girls are more involved in this than boys. Sniffing peaks at about 13 to 14 years and is more common in teenagers who also go out at night, skip school and have a large amount of pocket money.

The effects of sniffing include feelings of happiness, relaxation and drowsiness and last from 1 to 3 hours. Adolescents are largely unaware of the dangers in this practice, but sudden death can occur, even on the first occasion. In chronic abusers, depending on the solvent used, there may be damage to the nervous system, kidneys, liver or heart. It's dangerous stuff.

Analgesic use is very common, especially in secondary school girls, with around 30 per cent of fourth years using them at least weekly. This is extremely worrying because of the potential damage to kidneys (although analgesics can also cause stomach bleeding and anaemia). The girls' intake of pain killers (such as aspirin, panadol and codeine) rises particularly from the age of 13, presumably in relation to the onset of periods. Pain relief (if that's the reason for taking them) lasts 1 to 4 hours and if the preparation contains caffeine, it may cause a stimulant effect.

Stress-related symptoms to do with school and other pressures are also relevant, and provide the reason for many high school students taking tranquillizers. These are frequently abused by kids whose parents use them.

This problem doesn't come to doctors very often, but I did

learn something from one such instance. A bright and attractive, 15 year old girl was brought to see me, because she was behaving strangely in the classroom. She was actually stoned (with blurred vision, slurred speech and unco-ordinated limbs), having taken five tranquillizers for breakfast, apparently 'to brighten up her day'. With my encouragement, she owned up to her mother, who had been waiting patiently in the waiting room, but swore me to secrecy in regard to her older brother (who was 'really into the stuff').

A few days later, the whole family came along (Mother, Father and the two kids), but the discussion got nowhere. The girl could not remember me at all (or anything she'd said), the boy was mostly nodding off, and Mum and Dad maintained that 'everything's just fine'.

Marijuana use is illegal, which puts it into a different category. Around one in four secondary school and college students have used the stuff, its use rises with age and is associated with tobacco smoking (that is, kids are more likely to smoke marijuana if they already smoke tobacco). Parents worry that pot smoking puts teenagers on a downhill run to heroin. While you can't say this, because most use it as a recreational drug only, it does mean that they're likely to be in contact with people who peddle a variety of drugs, and this is a worry.

Meanwhile, heated debates about the ill effects of dope and whether or not it should be decriminalised, rage on. Given the controversy surrounding it, here is some up to date information: cannabis is best described as a mild intoxicant; it is not in itself an 'addictive' drug (meaning no physical dependence and no withdrawal symptoms are associated with it), and should not be linked with drugs like heroin, with which it has nothing in common; marijuana causes relaxation, laughter, increased appetite and a slowing down of time; there may be less pleasant effects such as dry mouth, dizziness, blood shot eyes and decreased co-ordination; the effects last 2 to 4 hours; a panic attack may occur in some users; chronic marijuana users become strongly psychologically dependent and refuse to believe that it is causing them harm; it also impairs short term memory, an effect that has important implications for students.

Marijuana is special in the following ways:

- Unlike other drugs of abuse, which are single chemicals (for example, alcohol, cocaine and LSD), marijuana contains 421 known chemicals, sixty-one of which are unique chemicals called 'cannabinoids' (only a handful of which have been studied)
- Unlike alcohol, which is water soluble (so its effects are washed out quickly from the body), cannabis accumulates in body fat; it takes about a month, for example, for all the chemicals in a single joint to clear from the body
- Unlike the cannabis in circulation 15 years ago, supplies now available have a higher content of delta-9-tetrahydrocannabinol (THC), the cannabinoid most responsible for the 'high'; there is also recent evidence to show that dried cannabis may be contaminated with fungi, creating a risk of fungal infection in the respiratory tract
- Unlike propagandists on both sides of the fence, scientists remain uncertain about the long term serious effects of even moderate use (although evidence is growing that marijuana can damage the lungs, heart, brain, immune system and reproductive organs)

Of more immediate concern is the fact that marijuana is just as dangerous to driving as alcohol. The combination of the two is totally devastating to anyone taking the wheel of a car.

How Can You Tell?

Young people take drugs for a variety of reasons: to get high (usually in a social setting), to gain relief from emotional pain, to go beyond the boundaries of ordinary experience, or simply to relax, lessen the pressure and slow down—the main reasons adults take drugs. Young people generally start off by experimenting with a drug (often to find out about the sensations it produces), but it becomes a habit when they think it solves their problems.

There is no precise profile of a drug taking adolescent (or anyone else, in fact). A lot depends on what they're taking, how much, and in what circumstances. Swings in mood and changes in behaviour patterns may be symptoms of drug abuse but, as we've seen, these may also be entirely normal. There are many alternative explanations: the hormonal changes of puberty, falling in love, having an argument with a best friend or feeling under pressure. However, the following, though not conclusive, are the signs to look for:

- A change in school attendance (frequently absent or late) or achievement (sloppy homework, apathy and lack of effort)
- Poor physical appearance and an extreme lack of regard for personal hygiene
- A marked change in emotional state with unusual aggressiveness or temper flare-ups or seeming excessively tired or withdrawn
- Furtive behaviour including lying, stealing or borrowing money (because drugs cost money)

If you suspect your kids are taking drugs, don't panic. Raise it with them as you would any other concern you had (this obviously goes for alcohol and tobacco too). Hopefully there will have been opportunities in the past to discuss the issue of drugs generally with them. Most teenagers are willing to talk about what's happening amongst their contemporaries, what they think about it and so on. If a teenager admits to using drugs, however, find out whether this is experimentation or regular use. Not only is detailed drug information only a phone call away, but there are counsellors who can advise and help you. Your local Community Health Centre is probably the best place to start.

The Plight of Homeless Youth

There must be very few parents who don't love their children, although some, for a variety of reasons, have difficulty expressing it in a positive way. People can be so caught up in their own troubles, that there is little left over for the kids. Some parents physically or sexually abuse their children. In some households, the level of tension and conflict is so great that living there becomes intolerable.

When a teenager runs away from home, it is frequently an act of desperation. Parents may be left bewildered, frightened, angry or worried. However, they are still at home, while the young person has generally walked 'out of the frying pan and into the fire'.

While a section on homeless youth is included here because of the high incidence of risk taking behaviour in this group, the issue itself should be of concern to all caring adults. It is a problem of overwhelming proportions, with an alleged 30 million homeless children or more throughout the world and thousands in all our major cities—and these are conservative estimates.

What must it be like to have nowhere to go, to think of home but feel unable to return there? Words like 'loneliness' and 'isolation' come to mind, but feelings go deeper than that. Young runaways (or throwaways as the case may be) typically have rock bottom self-esteem; many feel they have no history and have no sense of future, only a core of emptiness. Homeless teenagers grieve the loss of their families who may be out of sight, but are never for long out of mind. This is not something they discuss readily. Studies show that a majority of homeless kids have poor literacy and little skill in saying how they feel. Not only does it seem to them that 'nobody gives a damn', but they feel, and usually are, powerless to change their circumstances.

Homelessness is not in any way conducive to good health. 'Street kids' have little concern for self-care and have poor knowledge of their bodies and diseases. They tend to eat badly, sleep little and experience much stress, all of which interfere with normal growth and development. In their grim and often desperate struggle for survival, drugs, prostitution and violence become part of their world. In the longer term, many of them don't make it. They are vulnerable to infectious diseases such as hepatitis, gonorrhoea and AIDS. Deaths from suicides and motor vehicle accidents (perhaps one and the same) are not uncommon.

Teenage boys and girls in this situation need access to strong and caring adults, which is easier said than done. They tend to avoid hospitals and social workers and have little trust in the veritable army of 'do gooders' and authority figures. In youth refuges, they find exhausted, relatively young and generally unknowledgable workers, but rarely the stability and high quality support they crave. It is a monumental social problem.

What Can Be Done to Prevent Dangerous Risk Taking?

No one would suggest that all risk taking is problematic or even undesirable. If this were the message we were giving our kids, they might never climb a tree, ride a bike or bounce on a trampoline. Our concern here is about their getting out of their depth, about the potentially dire consequences of the sorts of health hazardous behaviour we've been discussing. We want to find ways to protect our kids from these.

You have to start early, encouraging children to understand and care for their bodies (which has a lot to do with how you look after yours). If parents are heavily into the medicine cabinet for the slightest ache or pain, or heavily into tobacco or alcohol, kids will take a leaf out of their book. Nothing surer. A heavy lecture on marijuana when a child turns 12 will not have the desired effect.

It is important to set limits for your kids. Negotiate with them about the time to be home, to be safe on the road, to avoid the temptation to drink too much. But remember, limits need to be constantly revised. What might be appropriate for a 15 year old is oppressive for a 17 year old.

Everything we discussed in terms of stress management (rehearsal, relaxation, self talk and assertiveness) in the previous chapter, is also relevant here. There is no special formula for preventing drug use amongst teenagers, or any other form of risk taking for that matter. Kids get together and do what they're going to do. Whatever it is, some will, some won't. Most of the happenings involving young people cannot be controlled by any heroic acts of parental will. In fact, having had your quiet and sensible say, established trust and maintained open communication, set the best example you can and prayed hard, the rest is really up to them.

What Else Can We Do?

At least four major areas of information—the mass media, the school, friends, and the family—contribute something to the problem areas of adolescent risk taking. Since there is so much community concern, perhaps there is a response that we, as parents, can make.

- A government can spend a great deal of public money (as ours is) on a lavish media campaign to raise community awareness about drugs, when it would take but a single piece of legislation to outlaw tobacco and alcohol advertising. (At the moment, however, this looks highly unlikely as the government relies on the revenue it brings.)
- School students represent a vast and impressionable captive audience for health education. Informed decision making is based on knowing the facts and weighing up the risks. There are skills available within the education system to put teenagers properly in the picture. Various bodies concerned with health and preventive health measures are certainly in favour of this approach. What we need now is the political will.
- Adolescents are desperate for clear and comprehensible information about themselves and the problems they face. When they cannot get this from adults, they have to make use of their own networks. Creative projects in which groups of young people are trained in both health issues and theatrical techniques, and then take thought provoking messages about health to teenagers in youth settings, have proved popular and successful. One such group (piloted during International Youth Year, 1985 in Australia), called itself 'Side Effects', was popular and had a measure of success after only 18 months. This type of peer education could be encouraged.

- Finally there are families, as always, left with the greatest responsibility of all. Parents have to psychologically immunise their kids against sinister influences in society and give them the resources, hopefully, to cope with pressure and adversity in constructive ways. Parents can do more, in fact, by getting together with other parents to learn about what to do, particularly in the area of preventing drug and alcohol abuse.

Conclusion

It's not just teenagers, you know. Older people indulge in risk taking too. Many things that adults do have negative health consequences in the longer term, but grownups are just more sedate about it. They may choose to eat a bad diet, to be sedentary, to innure themselves against stress with tranquillizers or to drink too much.

Young people, on the other hand, characteristically indulge in dangerous behaviour involving an immediate risk, and this can be their undoing. They take chances with sex, with self-neglect, with high speed, with sport and with substances of abuse. No wonder parents look forward to their growing up and slowing down. Then perhaps, at last, they can let out that long, lingering breath.

Homeless kids

CHAPTER THIRTEEN

Is There a Job Out There?

Having a job means having an answer when someone asks, 'What do you do for a living?' Getting a job is what's supposed to happen when you leave school or complete your training. It's what kids, and their parents, plan for and look forward to—a ticket to self-reliance, security and self-worth.

Unfortunately, whatever one's expectations or desires, there are no guarantees. While a good job can mean status, fulfilment and the chance for advancement, a bad job can mean stress, danger and boredom. The only thing worse, perhaps, is having no job at all!

The World of Work

For most teenagers, the world of work is school—that's where they are most of the week. Their whole effort is directed towards an imaginary afterwards. A badge I saw recently says, ever so simply, 'School's Out—What's Next?' This is the haunting question facing our kids from the moment they step into the secondary school years. Sadly, there are no longer any guarantees.

Early Forays

Children tune in to the harsh realities of the commercial world early in life. How long does it take for kids to realise that there are things to buy, from essential consumer items (such as bread,

WHEW! That's another batch delivered!
I'm going to be a MOVIE STAR!
I'm going to be an AIRLINE PILOT!
See any good jobs out there?
WELCOME TO THE REAL WORLD
GOOD JOBS (TERTIARY GRADS ONLY)
OTHER JOBS (MOSTLY BORING)
DOLE
S S EDUCATION
It's tough out there... I'm going back for more qualifications!

vegetables and so on) to commodities of more enduring value? At some point, what they really need is an income, and that means pocket money.

Pocket money is a financial handout which comes with or without strings attached. Family attitudes and practices vary widely here. Questions of how much, how often and what it's supposed to cover need to be resolved. Of course, the older the kid, the bigger the investment (a common source of irritation for younger siblings). I know of one father who puts a whole year's worth of pocket money into an account for each of his two teenagers, and lets them manage it as they see fit. (His 13 year old daughter is currently dabbling on the stock market.) Then there are those of us who are willing to be 'touched' on a weekly basis.

Many parents are wary of promoting the idea of 'something for nothing' and prefer to connect a regular allowance (or even sporadic payments) to the carrying out of certain household tasks. Alternatively, and more fairly, I think, a reasonable basic rate might be agreed to for sundry minor needs, with a bonus for voluntary duties. Whatever the system, pocket money introduces kids to the give and take of the commercial world, even though, in this instance, the 'boss' might be a bit of a pushover.

Adolescence can be expensive. A teenager's needs and desires (at least for all but the most indulged) will soon exceed the family coffers. Making a few dollars on the side becomes the only way to go. Enterprising kids look first within their immediate neighbourhood, taking virtually anything that pays—paper runs, babysitting, helping out at the local garage. For students, part time work after school or at weekends might involve a bit of travelling, but it shows a growing sense of responsibility and is generally worth encouraging.

What About a 'Proper' Job?

When it comes to looking at life, let alone future job prospects, the early teens make a high flying vantage point. Idealism is rampant and for most, anything seems within grasp. With the gaining of a little more maturity, say at 15 or 16, it is more a question of options, of weighing up possibilities (although fantasies about attractive lifestyles remain strong). Only later will kids become aware that high paying, sophisticated and exciting jobs are mostly figments of one's imagination. By the time it's OK to be practical, say at 18 or 19, aspirations will need to have shrunk to match a somewhat more sober reality.

Teenagers know that work is important. What we often forget to mention, unfortunately, is that a proper job, something a young person would be happy to stick at, is relatively hard to come by. A job that doesn't challenge one's abilities or afford an opportunity to explore and discover, can make arrival at the workplace a terrible disappointment.

The problem of youth underemployment gets relatively little attention. The pressure on young people to stay at school, obtain extra training and generally prepare themselves as extensively as possible for a better job later on, will provide definite advantages for some individuals (as well as keeping down the official unemployment figures). But what a let down, when the time eventually comes, for those who cannot find a job to match their qualifications.

Ever counted the number of pimples at supermarket checkouts or behind the sterile counters in fast food stores? Yes, they are filled with teenagers trying to earn even a little spare cash. There are jobs available for young people, but in terms of vocation, many leave a lot to be desired. If the only job a teenager can get is part time, there are two sides to the argument. On the positive side, one could argue (as employers might) that these jobs enable kids to learn the ropes, cope with people and achieve at least a small measure of self sufficiency. On the other hand:

- They don't constitute a totally adequate income
- They are frequently of a menial, repetitive and boring kind
- They represent only the most tenuous toe hold into the workforce
- They rarely lead to something enduring and worthwhile

The point is, as most parents will know, underemployment (even in a full time job) does little for human dignity, and rapidly turns youthful exuberance and enthusiasm to dust.

Worse Dangers than Boredom

Some years ago, I attended a conference on the health problems of adolescents, at which one of the speakers was an employer. I clearly remember the relatively dismal picture he painted of the adolescent in industry. With concern and consternation, he called our attention to the following: their dirty fingernails and poor general hygiene, their long hair (and the risk of scalping) and poor posture, their impaired hearing (from listening to loud music), their lousy diet, their non-conformity and poor regard for authority.

Oh boy! He was also troubled by their poor work performance, and, finally, by the number of accidents they had. As he spoke, I gained the impression that he found young people a bit of a trial, providing problems both for the boss and for themselves. Normal adolescent behaviour aside, for the reasons discussed in the previous chapter, young people are prone to health problems in the workplace (through their immaturity, lack of adequate preparation for the job, inexperience or risk taking behaviour). The consequences can be grave, with a disproportionately large number of young people being injured and killed in industry.

The World of No Work

Everyone is aware of the enormity of the youth unemployment problem. Many people are touched by it directly. With between one in four and one in five young people out of work, it is an issue that concerns kids, parents and governments. But the bald statistics give little sense of its impact on the lives of individuals and their families, and in general, the situation is not well understood.

Surely There's a Job Out There

Well, maybe there's *not* a job out there. But it's what a lot of people think. Comfortably employed people take a perfunctory glance at the fat employment sections in our major newspapers and wonder what all the fuss is about. Those who regularly do battle with these pages of promise, however, know differently. Changes in the job market over the past decade or so have been profound. With increasing technology, many full time jobs previously available to young people have simply disappeared. For those that remain, competition is fierce.

A government survey of the job market showed that 25 per cent of unemployed adolescents had trouble getting work because they were too young. Insufficient work experience ruled out another 10 per cent or so, in what has become the classic catch 22 for young job seekers: without a job, you can't get experience; without experience you can't get a job. It's not easy!

Young females are particularly vulnerable, with those aged between 15 and 19 years having less opportunity for employment than any other group in the country. As well as fewer jobs being available, there are also more restricted occupational choices for girls, a reflection, no doubt, of enduring sexism. And this is despite the fact that young women are reported to have higher educational status than young unemployed males.

What About Motivation?

One often hears adults talking about the laziness or lack of motivation of young people in regard to work. Employers say they have difficulty filling jobs at times, and accuse unemployed teenagers of being too choosy. Many parents seem to hold this view also, and believe that there are plenty of things kids could do if they really wanted to. Well, yes and no. It clearly depends on what side of the problem you're on.

Most young people who have been surveyed are very keen to work and gain experience. They are a very mobile group, often willing to travel long distances to seek employment. What they are always hoping for, of course, is to be able to do something useful, something they can feel good about. But what they do not always realise is that success requires more than motivation.

Other factors are important, for example: amount of schooling and academic achievement; current abilities; personality, attitude and appearance (that is, how you come across in interviews); and past work history. Unemployed kids with recent references from previous work fare better than those without. For unskilled workers, there just aren't a lot of jobs around, however keen you might be to find one.

Teenagers who do have jobs, on the other hand, are notorious for doing a half hearted job or just opting out, if things don't suit them. The boss, of course, experiences this as unreliability (which is the most common reason for young people losing their jobs). The big worry is that employers may ultimately feel disinclined to take on young people, thus adding immeasurably to the difficulties they face.

Motivation takes a beating too, when young people experience repeated or prolonged periods out of work. They become

depressed and demoralised by the vicious circle of unemployment. They become bored and listless, which makes it increasingly difficult to give a good impression at job interviews. So it's not surprising that the long term unemployed become increasingly unemployable.

What's It Like Being Unemployed?

Being unemployed for 2 weeks is like a holiday—being unemployed for 3 months, or 3 years, is like a sentence without a reprieve. Constantly looking for a job is an exhausting and disillusioning task in itself. As a young person who knows explains:

> I go to the Job Centre only to wait in line. I go to the Department of Health and Social Security only to wait in line. 'They' talk about statistics—I know what they mean—I'm just an unemployment statistic waiting in line.

The many difficulties that face out of work young people fall into three main categories: practical problems, health problems, and family problems.

Practical problems—Living on the dole, a single meagre cheque once a fortnight, provides for little more than a spartan existence. When the basics—rent or board, food and travel—are barely covered, anything you might want to do is limited by financial constraints. New clothes are often well beyond reach. A major problem is not having enough money to get around, which can lead to social isolation and loss of contact with friends. An unemployed 19 year old girl puts it like this—'When you can't afford to go anywhere, you're just stuck there. You feel confined'.

Health problems—Lifestyles that often accompany prolonged unemployment are not particularly healthy. Out of work young people admit to staying up late, not eating regularly or well, not exercising, smoking too much and drinking too much—behaviour related in part to simply having too much time on their hands. To be homeless as well greatly compounds the problems.

An unemployed 16 year old boy was referred to me by his local doctor, because he was feeling tired and dazed (sort of dizzy all the time). There wasn't anything specific to find, although he looked a bit pale and seedy. His daily timetable seemed relevant to his current state: during the week, he'd routinely sleep till about midday, have a bite to eat, then sit and watch television till midnight; on weekends, he'd go out with his friends and drink himself to oblivion. This had been his life since leaving school several months previously. He'd not tried to get a job and said he'd lost all confidence.

Unemployed young people are more likely to report health problems, both physical and emotional, then employed youth. Of these, emotional problems are considered the more serious:

- Unhappiness and depression have been widely reported, as well as increased suicide rates
- Feelings of loneliness, frustration, guilt and anxiety are commonly experienced

- Many have low self-esteem, an absence of goals and a lack of purpose in life
- Most feel alienated, powerless and disillusioned (a recipe for major social unrest and violence, as we've seen occurring in the United Kingdom)

Family problems—Looking to one's family, a traditional source of help and support, doesn't sound unreasonable. But this can be a big disappointment. Unemployed teenagers living at home often feel resentment at not being fully contributing members of the family. When they are nagged and hassled, as they often are, it adds insult to injury. They feel they have lost respect, that their parents see them as failures (which is exactly how they see themselves).

Parents also are frustrated and worried. They find it difficult to accept young people as adults when they don't have a proper job. It's aggravating when teenagers sleep in late, slop around the house like death warmed up, and don't seem to be making a major effort to get a job. Parents may resent having to support kids on the dole (particularly if they embrace an attitude of 'the world owes me a living'). They may be torn between feelings of helplessness, and an urge to force them into some sort of employment, 'for their own good'. (Some parents give this as a reason for taking a big chunk of the dole as board—a measure more likely to be experienced as punitive than helpful.)

Arguments and tension can reach the point where leaving home may seem preferable to enduring the hassles or shame. Some kids are literally thrown out, often to face worse and deteriorating circumstances (which frequently include joining the pathetic ranks of the homeless). But it doesn't always end up like this and it doesn't need to. Some families seek more constructive solutions and cope better—they encourage unemployed young people to maintain hope and accept that the overall problem is not of their making (which it most definitely is not).

Parental Hopes

Very few parents would not want their kids to find a niche, to end up doing something worthwhile. Many have hopes and aspirations, sometimes in multiple areas of their children's lives—relationships, hobbies, and of course, career. Some parents have it all worked out. To them, children are not just little kids with a future of their own (as uncertain as that may be). At 3 years of age, they are already doctors, lawyers or business tycoons.

Such children bear the promise of becoming what their parents could not be, of achieving what their parents could not achieve. Some people merely want their offspring to follow along in their own footsteps, to validate and continue their parents' efforts. Parents who live through their kids put them under enormous pressure, and it can work out badly.

An 18 year old boy with crippling stomach pains told me that he desperately wanted to choose a different career path to his father's, but couldn't muster up the courage to tell him. (Eventually he did and then pursued his own interest.) I know of other cases in which bright and talented young people have opted out of further education rather than following a prescribed professional career. Teenagers need to develop a separate and special identity of their own, but hopefully not a life path determined by an act of rebellion.

All parents wonder what lies ahead for their kids. In today's world, to not worry about this would be unusual. It's impossible

not to be involved, to enjoy their successes and suffer their failures. At the same time, we should allow them to live and create their own reality. We can be supportive, but we cannot do it for them.

Finding Employment

Parents may or may not have had to look for a job themselves in recent years, but it will be an enormous help to your son or daughter if you can provide some specific guidance about how to go about it. At the outset, they need to know what to expect when they register with the Job Centre. The people there are there to advise on what jobs are available (and their requirements), their eligibility for various government work/education and apprenticeship training schemes, where self-help groups for unemployed youth are located, travel concessions and so on.

Teenagers may also need assistance, at first, in writing an appropriate letter of application and preparing a c.v. But the most important thing they have to realise is how crucial it is to present well in person. A student counsellor, Jan Wilson, offers young people some practical hints for the interview:

- Make an effort to create a good first impression

- Be neat and clean: old plimsolls or trainers, excess makeup or super-trendy clothes can prejudice an employer
- Have available in a folder: your school records, any certificates or special awards, references, any samples of past writing or hobby which may be relevant
- Arrive 5 minutes early; do not become impatient if you are kept waiting (the employer may be delayed)
- When asked to enter, step forward and speak clearly, be prepared to shake hands, do not sit until asked to do so
- Always look directly at the interviewer
- Do not smoke unless invited to do so—preferably not at all

Some Unanswered Questions

As incredible as it sounds, a growing percentage of bright, able bodied and eager young people face the prospect of a future without work. At one time, such an idea would have seemed preposterous. Today it is a reality, a situation brought about by our new technologies and changing priorities.

What we are seeing is the creation of a new social condition in which an increasing number of young people are frozen in limbo between school and work. What was already a long period of dependence on parents is being extended. In our society, so much of one's identity is wrapped up in work. Without it, there is no way to avoid feeling like a second class citizen.

Unemployment is clearly a complex social problem with far reaching consequences. For one thing, it renders the traditional function of schools invalid. Should we, in the light of current reality, be educating kids for unemployment? Or is that a defeatist attitude? There are a number of other pertinent and perplexing questions as well:

- Does long term unemployment always have negative effects on young people? Not necessarily—the research on this remains inadequate. There are very few studies that follow young people from school into unemployment and note the changes. Surely it is wrong, therefore, to assume that all unemployed young people will regress, deteriorate or self-destruct. Some will maintain social competence, while others will strike out in new, effective directions (a tribute to an indomitable human spirit?).

- Are we sometimes confusing cause and effect? For example, perhaps a young person is unemployed by virtue of being strange or inadequate (not being able to relate to people, for example), rather than being strange and inadequate by virtue of being unemployed. A couple of young men, patients of mine with medical conditions, have had jobs temporarily and lost them, ostensibly because they were 'too slow'.
- Is it possible that some young people find temporary advantage in the role of unemployment, as a respite from academic or social pressures perhaps? Taking a break from work and living on the dole (particularly when several incomes are pooled) is not all that tough. In fact, the unemployment benefit was first introduced as a stopgap between jobs (it was never intended as a permanent lifestyle). Needless to say, those few dishonest individuals who live well on several dole cheques, bring discredit and dishonour to their struggling peers.

Conclusion

A hobby has been described as 'hard work you wouldn't do for a living'. Of course, if you can manage to be paid for something you enjoy as much as a hobby, you're fortunate indeed—you're part of a small and privileged minority.

Throughout the world, studies of young peoples' worries about the future put unemployment into first place. Society has to find a satisfactory solution to this and not merely accept it as part of the inevitable cost of progress. The ultimate consequences of disrupting, confusing and alienating an entire generation of energetic young people is surely a high price to pay.

CHAPTER FOURTEEN

Letting Go

By the time your children turn into teenagers, you've come a long way as a parent, and there's much to be proud about. Those treasured baby photos and the ones of little puffed out cheeks over smoking birthday candles bear testimony to less complex times. These memories are to be enjoyed, because parenting adolescents is not easy!

For one thing, life is less predictable. At no other time in the family life cycle is there likely to be more uncertainty and confusion. Parents may approach their children's teenage years with elation or with apprehension, but few are prepared for the feelings of bewilderment, sadness and inner conflict that frequently arise. Providing guidance and support, while at the same time progressively loosening the reins of control, is the nature of the challenge.

Letting Go When You Want to Hold On

Armed with good advice and goodwill, I once watched my young teenage daughter bounce down a train station ramp and head off to spend a weekend in the country with friends—not unreasonable in itself, but at the time, a bit of a wrench for me. More recently, we planned a family outing and had high expectations of a great day. Thirteen year old son 'regretfully' announced: 'Sorry folks, guess I'll have to give it a miss—other plans'.

As a parent, one has to bear many small losses in order to gain a greater prize—a mature and self-sufficient young person who

All right...
but promise you
won't fly where
we can't see you,
you know how your
father worries!

can relate to you, ultimately, as an adult. But the process of separation is painful, and there is ambivalence about it on both sides.

As teenagers move increasingly within their own circles and do more and more their own way, we are called upon to adjust to a progressive loss of status and a lessening of control. This is unsettling. But holding onto poignant memories of how they were as little kids is to no avail, for we cannot turn back the clock. On the other hand, the future is uncertain and many parental fears are rooted in reality. We will not always be there to smooth the way.

Learning to Trust

There is no simple knack to letting go. Certainly it is not an all or none phenomenon, but rather a gradual relinquishing of control over time. It has been said that 'raising children is like baking bread; it has to be a slow process or you end up with an overdone crust and an underdone interior'.

So much depends on it and yet, for most of us, letting go almost goes against our every, caring fibre. An American psychologist, Haim Ginott, has said it well: 'This can be our finest hour. To let go when you want to hold on requires utmost generosity and love. Only parents are capable of such painful greatness'.

Absolutely right. And how does one achieve this state of grace? Much of it lies in *learning to trust*. Teenagers need a parent's trust in order to be themselves and to become responsible for themselves. Giving it, however, is somewhat less straightforward. Consider some of the difficulties involved:

- How do you trust a teenager whom you're certain is up to no good? Shifty eyes and convoluted stories don't make it easy
- How do you trust a kid who constantly hands you the implausible line, 'But everybody's doing it/going there/sleeping over . . .?
- How do you trust a teenager when the people with whom they keep company raise all sorts of suspicions in your

mind? (As a mother said to her daughter, 'In you, I have all the faith in the world, it's the other people in the world I have trouble with')

- How do you trust a kid who's got *you* as a parent? You certainly remember what you did when you were that age?!

This is a dilemma. Parents know that their offspring are gullible, that there are all sorts of dangers to their health, safety and peace of mind. But whatever the reasons, lack of trust is no secret. Certain behaviours loudly proclaim it: asking too many questions; nagging and lecturing; showing overprotective concern. From time to time, we are all guilty of these things. For teenagers, however, they are high on the list of 'most abhorred parental traits'.

What do you do? Occasionally it is necessary to literally bite your bottom lip and quietly sit on your misgivings. It can pay off. I tried this once by not 'suggesting' that our eldest daughter miss an outing on Saturday night in honour of the exam on Monday. She made this decision herself without any help at all. Teenagers like to feel trusted and generally live up to the expectation. In a

Most abhorred parental trait

vicious circle of happy outcomes they'll make better choices and more mature judgements and you'll be able to worry less and everything should work out fine. (Well, that's the theory, anyway.)

Of course, misplaced trust is disappointing. On occasion, you'll actually realise you've been lied to. Kids sometimes start out with a small deception or thoughtful omission and a major fabrication builds from there to cover up. With your first born, this always seems worse (you become wiser later). It's generally better not to completely fall apart. You could perhaps say something powerful like, 'I'd like to know why you felt you couldn't tell me the truth'. Then proceed to outline the consequences.

I'm Sleeping at So and So's House

An adolescent phenomenon requiring a good deal of parental trust is sleeping over at a friend's place. Almost all teenagers (and many younger children too, of course) want to do this, and increasingly as they get older. It's normal. It's wonderful too, sometimes, to have them out of the house. But sleeping out does raise some parental concerns, simply because you're out of the picture. For one thing, you are trusting them to be where they say—hopefully with people you know or know something about. You won't know what time they get in if they go out. The next day, you'll wonder if they got any sleep—when you see them, it won't be hard to tell.

The mother of a 16 year old boy described her reaction when she received a call from his 14 year old girlfriend, at 9.00 pm, saying that he was 'too tired to come home'. When he eventually got to the phone, he sheepishly announced, 'It has been suggested that I stay the night'. His mother, not amused, 'suggested' that if he didn't appear at their front door in 15 minutes, she'd be down to collect him.

I know some parents who do not permit their kids to sleep over at all, often for logistical reasons (too complicated with lots of children; too much chauffeuring around etc) However, most parents do permit it, viewing it as part of their exploration of the world out there, of seeing how the other half lives. Obviously, it is also part of a normal desire to gain distance from you. All that remains to be resolved is when and how often. School nights would probably be out (Sunday nights too) and not around exam time. Every other night away would probably be too often. As always, it's a personal decision. However, one helpful solution is to telephone the other parent involved. That way, some of your fears and concerns can be allayed.

The Ubiquitous Party

What if it's all happening at your place? If ever you want to experience shell shock, allow your teenager to throw a rip roaring party at home. The noise and mess are the least of it—you expected that anyway. But you are there in the responsible role of adult chaperone (a euphemistic expression if ever there was one). Not unreasonably, you might wonder about the following:

- Who's there? Don't ask. Probably more kids than were invited; they're physically bigger than you imagined and generally disinclined to give you the time of day (which is disappointing if you personally prepared the food and helped with the decorations)
- What are they doing when you can't see them? Don't ask. Even if you wander around 'unobtrusively' all night offering savouries, you'll never keep track of them; there's outside too, you know
- There isn't any alcohol here, is there? Don't ask. That was *the deal*, but check around in the morning—you'll discover what sort of 'do' you really had. And it's best not to serve punch (as some clown is sure to lace it!)

Only after having this experience myself (with 16 and 17 year olds), and talking about it with other parents, did I fully realise what a contentious issue it is. Parents worry about teenage parties, suspecting that having fun might mean more than just hot dogs, innocent games and loud music. Sex, alcohol and goodness knows what else is the combination we fear. Some people simply refuse to have teenage parties, preferring to let it be somebody else's headache. However, if you are willing to play host or hostess, (the preferable attitude, I would say), there are three main positions you can take:

The party

Exercise militant control—insist on a guest list and tick off kid's names as they enter the house, introduce everybody to the bouncer, give out printed rules about expected behaviour and proposed punishments for transgressors. (This approach is only appropriate for a 'one off' affair as no kid would want to come to a party at your place again)

Go out for the night—that is, let them get on with it and hope for the best (the furniture needs replacing anyway); it might be a good idea, however, to let the police know where they can contact you, and to expect to hear from them

Be there and be fair—most parents would probably seek the middle ground. This involves: negotiating beforehand what's acceptable and what's not (alcohol, for one), agreeing to maintain a friendly 'arm's length' presence and *trusting* your offspring and his or her friends (hopefully excluding gate crashers) to be a bit responsible. Mostly, it works out OK

Those Outside Influences

While we're on this subject of trust, a word of reassurance about the apparently growing influence of 'outsiders'. Teenagers undoubtedly look to their peers in matters concerning their appearance, leisure activities and other interests of youth. But the evidence seems to indicate that they still tend to turn to their parents for guidance on major questions of values. In a large English study, the vast majority of 14 and 15 year olds believed their parents approved of their friends. Do you?

Parents sometimes resent other adults who appear to assume importance in their kids' lives, despite realising that alternative authority figures can be valuable resources at this time. Teenagers are fortunate to have access to caring adults other than their parents.

Holding On

Some parents let go too quickly and push kids out. There are subtle ways to do this, for example, through disinterest or neglect. People who are particularly keen to get on with their own lives may prematurely retreat from parental responsibilities.

More commonly, however, there is reluctance to give up the reins, and this can be taken to extremes. Some parents may want to hold onto their children because the alternative is to face new priorities or a new middle aged identity. If things are not too secure between spouses, teenagers often provide a necessary distraction. This too can generate a desire or need to hold on more strongly than is desirable.

The following parental syndromes, all rooted in the needs and personalities of adults, add to the difficulties of growing up:

Overcontrol—in which 'care and concern' is expressed as mollycoddling or 'military might'. Some parents feel they have the right to plan and direct every aspect of a child's life. Not surprisingly, undue parental influence rarely works out well.

For the young person with little room to move (an extremely stressful situation to be in), there are several options: to react

against it in a normal sort of way (a healthy rebellion); to escape the feeling of being boxed in by getting involved in drugs or some other sort of risk taking behaviour (an unhealthy rebellion); by abdicating and fitting into the mould set by parents (at the expense, unfortunately, of individual creativity).

Overexpectation—in which parental pressure to achieve or perform leads to a submerging of a child's personal interests or initiatives. When a 12 year old kid rushes up to her mother and says, 'Mum, I've just figured out how you can be a lot happier with me—lower your expectations', she's not joking.

Some parents programme their children to behave in certain ways and often live vicariously through them. Yehudi Menuhin's parents got away with it, but most don't. I recall an overweight 13 year old girl whose mother had desperately wanted her to be a ballet dancer. Her efforts to urge this highly valued personal goal onto her daughter had led to the girl's opting out by overeating.

No one would question the desirability of giving young people high ideals, but it is preferable not to push them beyond their abilities or personal interests. (Perhaps it is enough that they do just twice as much or as well as other kids.) The idea, in fact, is to match one's expectations with the likelihood of success—another of those balancing acts for which you have received no training.

Overindulgence—in which kids are allowed to get away with murder. In the words of Thomas Szasz, 'permissiveness is the principle of treating children as if they were adults; and the tactic of making sure they never reach that stage'. Ironically, overindulgence is also a form of holding on. A parental attitude that lacks firmness fails to provide a model for an adolescent to either identify with or rebel against, and confusion prevails. Whilst they rarely admit it openly, most children are looking for firmness.

What About Problem Kids?

Let's not view this whole issue in terms of parents not doing the right thing. It's more complicated than that. Teenagers have to co-operate with this gradual lessening of outside control and be willing to gradually assume greater responsibility for themselves. Some teenagers, by virtue of being immature, depressed or unwell, for example, are too dependent and want to stay attached to the apron strings. They are not progressing normally. Beware too of the perfect kid, for the road to healthy adolescent development is never completely smooth.

On the other hand, some young people are too independent and take off too soon or too far. If this is a personality trait, you will have seen it coming for a long time. It's a bit awkward, however, if you've let children have a free reign throughout childhood. By adolescence, they will have become used to calling the shots, and trying to tighten up on discipline now will be fraught with difficulty.

Taking a Stand

Leadership takes courage. As parents, you can survive being unpopular. There are times when you have to grit your teeth and say, 'This is the way it has to be', because, while trust is vital, it does not mean that anything goes. In fact, children feel distinctly insecure, and will come to interpret it as a lack of caring, if limits are not clearly set (which is different from being rigid).

Not having limits is like riding a bicycle across a narrow bridge with no railings. More importantly, during adolescence, kids need limits to test themselves against and feel secure within. They need to know, at least, what a parent thinks on a particular issue. As one teenager put it, 'If I don't know what my parents think, how can I do the opposite?'

Important Matters

On some matters, certainly the important ones, parents have to take a stand. You can always compromise on less world shattering issues, such as where the soap is supposed to be put in the bathroom. But when it comes to things like moderate behaviour in public or contributing something to family life, the expectations should be clear.

Rules and responsibilities define a household. They prescribe a family's particular way of living together. In fact, a cohesive family in which the child is expected to play a positive, clearly defined role is said to be the strongest thing a kid has going for it. In general, the better the family works, the better chance he or she has of making it in life.

Limits are not idle threats, harsh and unreasonable demands or 'here today and gone tomorrow' suggestions. Effective limits are firm, fair, explicit and consistent, and this is what we should aim for. However, limits do need to change over time. There's no special way to do this and personal views vary greatly. What most parents find is that they need to renegotiate around particular events. As teenagers grow up, there's always something new to contend with and a way (your way) to deal with it.

Mandatory Retirement

In a personal, hand crafted birthday card to me, my 16 year old daughter included this saying for 1986—'As teenagers grow older, adulthood is no longer pretended; and thanks to understanding parents, their curfews are extended'.

Curfews are a good example of limit setting and a common source of conflict in families. I know of one father who gave his daughter a key to the front door on her fifteenth birthday, and simply asked her to be quiet when she came in. Most parents feel more comfortable with an agreed upon time. As one young adolescent said, 'In my house we have mandatory retirement—I have to be in bed by 10.00 pm'.

There's a qualitative difference between turning in and coming in. A desire to have our kids safely under wraps at a reasonable hour is based on several factors:

- A need to know they are safe
- A need to get a decent night's sleep ourselves
- A concern about behaviour that may put them at risk (sex, drugs, overtiredness)
- A conviction (probably based on the story of Cinderella) that there are greater dangers after the witching hour

Whatever the reasons, it is a parent's prerogative to achieve an understanding about this and it can be approached in one of two ways:

- 'You will be home by midnight or else . . !'—a no nonsense, authoritarian approach that usually buys trouble in the form of resentment or rebellion. It also does little to encourage self-responsibility (which is, after all, the goal of discipline).
- 'What time will you be getting home?' or 'What time do you think would be reasonable?'—a basis for negotiation. A mutually acceptable arrangement can usually be arrived at, a better outcome for all concerned and more likely to be adhered to.

Some aspects of parenting never change. There is nothing outdated about needing to establish where kids are spending their

Setting limits

outside time and with whom, and how and when they will get home. The mother of a 16 year old girl states her case in this straightforward way: 'I want to know where you are. While we're together, we're accountable to each other. Would you like it if I were to go off for three days and you didn't know where I was?'

Logical Consequences

Allied to the skill of setting firm, clear limits is knowing what to do when they are breached. This is tricky, and the older the teenager, the harder it gets. There is much written about the importance of logical consequences. The idea is that transgressions are transformed into learning experiences. This means allowing (or insisting, if necessary) that outcomes, having relevance to the 'crime', occur. Ideally, this will have been happening throughout childhood so that kids can progressively gain a sense of internal control, or at least know what to expect in a given set of circumstances.

A 14 year old daughter took one of her father's favourite shirts to a school camp, and returned, 9 days later, without it. 'It's missing!' Dad was infuriated, more by her *laissez faire* attitude than by the loss itself. The girl had shared a dormitory with a dozen or so other girls. 'Maybe one of them took it by mistake', she shrugged.(In a world with starvation and strife, for goodness' sake, it's only a shirt.) The incensed father insisted that she contact each and every girl and get it back. (It's his shirt and there's a principle at stake.)

This is an example of logical consequences. An alternative punishment, such as having to wash up for a week, would not have carried the message, 'if you lose something belonging to someone else, at least make an effort to find it'. But what if there's not an obvious flow on from the teenager's misdemeanour? This calls for creativity, and possibly some help from the culprit. One might ask, 'Which of the following activities or privileges would you care to forgo?' Up front, you're seeking to be reasonable (although your thoughts might be running to grounding the kid for 25 years).

Harmony and Conflict

Are you polite to your children? This is an important question and one, like responsive listening, that is frequently taken up in parenting guides. Who would dare suggest that this is anything but highly desirable? As a major pillar of parenting, however, there are one or two flaws. The following examples are representative of good advice one might read or hear about this issue:

- 'Treat your kids as you would treat guests in the house'—this would be fine if they behaved like guests and left after an appropriate period; it also sounds like a good way to turn them into strangers
- 'Don't yell at the kids, it's not nice to be screamed at'—of course it's not, and there are certainly more effective ways to express anger; but parents usually don't 'talk loudly' for nothing . . .
- 'Practise using firm but friendly facial expressions and gestures in front of the mirror'—but don't let anybody see you, they'll send for a strait jacket

In reality, there cannot be amicable and positive interaction between parents and teenagers at all times. If there is, an awful lot is being suppressed. Nevertheless, some parents become distraught in the face of ordinary adolescent back chat, occasional bad language, or the many other subtle (and not so subtle) signs that teenagers are wanting emotional separation. They try to gain distance in this way in order to see themsleves more clearly.

Not that it doesn't hurt. Adolescents have an uncanny, sixth sense about how to put the boot in, and being on the receiving end is not at all pleasant. Better that our self-esteem is not totally tied up in what our kids think of us or say to us, for if it is, we're in for hell. What we must tell ourselves, often, is that such behaviour is developmentally normal (clearly, easier said than done).

What If You're Really Angry?

A father had become very angry with his two teenage sons, and would let them know about it, often, in no uncertain terms. Mostly, they were just being adolescent (giving a bit of cheek, taking their time over chores and so on). This dad was a screamer, and the fact that Mum generally sided with the kids added to his frustration, sadness and disappointment. He felt that he had tried to do his best by them and considered them grossly unappreciative.

This is not an uncommon scene. Parents frequently fight about how to discipline and generally deal with teenagers. In the above instance, the mother believed that the father's behaviour was causing the boys' behaviour. While it probably was a factor, it is more likely that the boys were acting out the marital difficulties. If these parents were able to stop blaming each other long enough to find some middle ground (or get help if there seemed not to be any), their mutual support might go a long way to easing the intergenerational conflict as well.

Some conflict is normal. When there is a lot of anger involving parents and teenagers, however, it may be serving as an alternative to experiencing pain (the emotional kind). As teenagers and their parents separate, these feelings inevitably surface. On both sides there will be sadness. Elizabeth Kubler Ross has made us aware of the anger involved in normal bereavement. So it makes sense that, for some people, it is easier to fight to stay together, than face the feelings of loss associated with moving apart.

Of course, when the fighting becomes inexorable or is tinged with cruelty, or when it starts to affect the health of a family member or extends outside the family (school failure, for example), it is time to take stock. Someone (perhaps Mum and Dad together) needs time out, or the family needs professional help.

A Gift for Life

A 50 year old man confided in a friend that he wasn't doing too well in business, 'I'm not surprised really, Dad always said I'd never make a go of it'. The concept of self-fulfilling prophecy should be constantly on our minds where our children are concerned. In a very real sense, we are helping to mould their future lives.

The value of positive reinforcement is too often underestimated. It is as vital a fuel for self-esteem as air is for life. The beliefs and attitudes we have about ourselves as individuals are acquired early, but the need for personal validation remains with us forever. Our feelings of self-worth require care and maintenance.

For parents, there are some basic dos and don'ts that have stood the test of time. Teenagers' self-esteem is not likely to be enhanced by the following:

- Being compared to other kids you know, their siblings or, worst of all, you as a teenager
- Being deluged with 'righteous goodness' in the form of nagging, lecturing or moralising; parents who do this all the time belong to the 'excessive virtue' group and are most likely to dominate teenagers through overcontrol and overexpectation
- Being verbally put down: 'you're a clumsy idiot just like your father'; 'the trouble with you, you little twerp, is that you've got no self-esteem'
- Being flippantly dismissed, 'don't be so bloody ludicrous'

More than anything else, young people want to be listened to, trusted, and given respect as individuals. Despite the ambivalent messages they sometimes give, they do want their comments and ideas to be taken seriously, and they do want the people who are important to them to take an interest in their lives and activities. You can study a hundred self-help books or take a thousand courses. But in the final analysis, liking your son or daughter and letting it show will ultimately carry the day.

In fact, fostering healthy self-esteem in our children is probably our single most important task as parents. This is not a time consuming exercise. As Dr Spencer Johnson suggests in *The One Minute Mother* (Columbus Books, 1984), '. . . catch them doing something right'. A well timed word, a well placed touch may be all that is required to convey the message, 'you are a capable and competent person; your assets and strengths show'. It's worth it. To grow up being able to feel good about yourself is, after all, a gift for life.

Memories

I asked a father of three children what he enjoyed most about being a parent. He replied, 'reliving each and every stage of childhood with them'. He's lucky to be enjoying it, as this is not always a pleasant or easy process. We may not even be consciously aware that it's happening, but it is impossible to avoid. From time to time, something will trigger an image or feeling from our own past. Occasionally, parents have to relive and perhaps better understand something important that happened to them many years ago.

Feelings From the Past

Since every, single experience we ever have is retained in the recesses of our mind, this is not all that surprising. Perhaps you're playing with your 4 year old child and suddenly you're remembering how delicious it was to lick an ice-cream that hot summer, or how nice it was to rush out to greet the fruit and vegetable man as he came slowly down your street.

On the other hand, helping my 11 year old daughter with her homework recently had me thinking about the time, when I was about her age, when I lied to a teacher about having completed something I hadn't even started. His look of weary scepticism is as vivid today (as is my guilt) as if it had happened yesterday.

Becoming a parent reactivates many old conflicts, many of them to do with our own parents. 'The trouble with parents', someone kidded, 'is that it's hard to think of them as people'. Just because they've lived longer than you, they always know best (even when you're fully grown); they may say and do the most outrageous things, and get hurt if you don't seem to understand that it's basically for your own good; and they can never quite believe, many of them, that you are actually capable of making a go of it, doing things your way.

As I mentioned before, you become a parent, but you remain a son or daughter. Emotionally, there are always unresolved bits and pieces from your earlier life. Harold Bloomfield says, 'Conflicts you had with your parents may reappear in the conflicts you have with your children'. Parenting, it seems has a powerful hold on your life.

Not Enough to Go On

Meanwhile, lots of things have changed. The social climate in which our children are growing up today is profoundly different to that of 3 short decades ago. In the words of journalist/author, Phillip Adams, 'The world was simple (then), the pace was slow and the pressures were minimal . . . . the clock on the classroom wall seemed to have stopped'. Nostalgia may have blurred our recollections somewhat, but it does seem that there was a greater sense of continuity and coherence; a feeling that life was generally more settled.

While you may have fond memories of relaxed, Saturday afternoon matinées, meccano sets and careering down a hill on a home made go-kart, kids today are entertained by computer games with synthesised sound effects, walkman radios and expensive skate boards. More importantly, you may have managed to remain a virgin till 25—many teenagers now become sexually active at 15! They are also taller, stronger, and better developed and have many different ideas and aspirations.

The point is simply this: 'when I was young . . .' has lost its clout. Your personal experience of adolescence (20 or 30 years ago or whatever) is not enough to go on, things have changed too much. Of course, this has always been the case. In the past 80 years or so, there hasn't been a single decade in which parents were not confused about how to behave, about how best to raise their children.

Prevailing attitudes to discipline, for example, have changed dramatically: the popularity of spanking has come and gone (and is definitely 'out' at present); reasoning with kids or just loving them and hoping for the best, have also seen their day. And by about 1970, a new feeling was emerging—'to hell with them!' The 'me generation' arrived on the scene, coinciding, it seemed, with parents' confidence in their ability to succeed as parents reaching an all time low. Parents who felt they had nothing to offer would express feelings towards their teenagers such as, 'It's your life, you live it the way you want to'.

A decade or so on, and the feeling has changed yet again. Our memories may not be enough to go on, but we're more aware of what's going on and more optimistic. Here we are, knowing so much about how kids grow and learn; realising that our words and actions affect their feelings and behaviour; accepting the creed of firmness and fairness; and understanding that our own personal needs are important too.

It's good to be a parent now. Freed from the tyranny of perfection, parents can now be *good enough* and take the good with the bad. Our view of our kids and ourselves can, at last, be more balanced and reasonable.

Conclusion

The suggestion that there is a right way to raise children of any age is clearly ridiculous. This notion has been aptly called the 'myth of parenthood' and is responsible for a great deal of unnecessary self-flagellation and guilt. I am not the first to note that children, parents, and the issues they face, separately and together, cannot be forced into a formula. For each teenager and each parent, there is a need to learn together, to work things out over and over again.

By the way, since nobody finds the parenting of teenagers easy, you may derive some comfort from knowing that 'experience is a wonderful thing—it enables you to recognise a mistake when you make it again'. We can only do our best. Try not to be too hard on yourself and, above all, don't despair!

APPENDIX

Who Can Help?

You, the parent, are a very important person in your teenager's life. Simply by being there and letting your kids know that you love and value them, you are providing something irreplaceable. But let's face it, parenting teenagers takes energy and forbearance. The experience is immersing at least; exasperating and exhausting at worst. Although most parents do reasonably well most of the time, it's the other times that get us down. Here are some additional ideas about who can help.

What Are Friends For?

Parents are notoriously reluctant to ask for help. This is probably because it makes us feel ashamed to admit that we're not coping, or not entirely sure what to do. It's nicer to come across as super-confident, as though everything were perfectly under control. Also, through some mental aberration, we imagine that other families aren't facing exactly the same dilemmas.

Where parenting teenagers is concerned, however, comparing ideas and approaches is almost always illuminating and helpful. Not only does the process of sounding-off in safe surroundings feel good, and help you get things into perspective (after all, what are friends for?), but it also frees you from that terrible sense of isolation that parents often feel.

Parents can also learn from each other that some issues are worth a major hassle and some are not. What's more, you should not underestimate your own experience—your personal approach to a situation or problem may be extremely useful to somebody else.

More Organised Encounters

From time to time (or regularly in some instances), educational evenings on topics of interest to parents are organised by schools, churches or community groups. Usually there is a guest speaker or a panel, followed by questions or comments from the floor. Rarely are such events not packed out. Attending a talk or seminar is a relatively painless way to get in touch with the current thinking of experts and the views of other parents. You can always ask a tricky question about a problem concerning someone else's kid!

Drawing on the combined insights, ideas and skills of a group of parents meeting in more intimate circumstances can also be worthwhile. By getting together, with or without a trained group leader, parents can inform and support each other. What many people don't seem to realise is that there doesn't have to be a crisis before you look for help. Don't think that because your teenager isn't into hard drugs, failing in school or getting arrested, that you shouldn't avail yourself of such opportunities. Taking part in a proper discussion on parenting may turn out to be one of the most valuable experiences you will ever have. Of the various courses on parenting that are available, the following are probably the best known:

Parent Effectiveness Training (P.E.T.), launched by American psychologist Thomas Gordon in 1963, has a wide-ranging influence; it teaches parents skills that will help them get along with their children: active listening (trying to extract unspoken messages from the child's words); 'I-messages' rather than 'you-messages'; 'no-lose' problem solving. Essentially, P.E.T. stresses non-threatening, non-judgemental communication between parent and child. People 'in training' report that their children are often bemused, at the outset at least, by a sometimes sudden change in communication style. But, for motivated people, such courses provide essential tools for dealing with common difficulties.

Systematic Training for Effective Parenting of Teens (STEP/Teen), by American psychologists Don Dinkmeyer and Gary D. McKay. Like P.E.T., this course comes with a guide, which you can work at alone or as a member of a group. Each week for ten weeks, you would be encouraged to address specific issues arising between parents and teenagers, practising and implementing relevant skills. These include: handling emotions, building your teen's self esteem, communication, discipline and conducting a family meeting.

Of course, highly structured programmes are not everybody's cup of tea. Some of the methods pose facile and simplistic solutions to complex problems, while some problems are ignored altogether. Some people simply balk at the prospect of techniques, viewing them as manipulative or unrealistically rigid. The important thing to remember, however, is that the underlying principles are sound and there is always something useful to be gained. You can learn to understand yourself and your family better, and learn ways of relating that are likely to work for you.

When More Is Needed

Some problems facing parents and teenagers are serious and are not amenable to parenting skills alone. It's not always easy to tell when outside help is necessary, and it's a personal matter anyway. But if the situation is worrying and ongoing, whatever it is, all it takes is a telephone call to set the ball rolling.

Actually, it's not always quite that simple. One way and another, in *Growing Pains*, we've touched on a lot of issues related to the health and well-being of young people, as well as some of the special difficulties facing parents in their own lives. These are often interconnected, but finding a resource that is able to take a broad view of the situation is often difficult. Services catering to teenagers are rather fragmented (if they exist at all). Let's take a look at what is available and what isn't.

Where to Start

Depending on the problem, your first port of call will probably be one of the following:

- Your **family doctor** who is in an excellent position to provide accessible, broad based and, when appropriate, confidential health care for teenagers, as well as for the whole family

- The **local hospital** via casualty or, in ideal circumstances, a medical/counselling service
- The **school psychologist** is a mental health resource to students and often helpful adviser to parents (although they are spread thinly and not in a position to offer treatment to families)—teachers who know your teenager well can also be useful
- Your **minister of religion** who may have training in pastoral counselling
- Your local **community health centre** which offers a wide range of medical and psychosocial care, information and support (for example, discussion groups) for parents and teenagers and may include groups for those from non-English speaking backgrounds

As a rule, these established resources will be able to help you or, if not, advise where you can get help. You can also take a look at your *Yellow Pages* or at leaflets and so on at your library or doctor's surgery.

Special Situations

With certain problems, there are more specific avenues to explore as well. What's available essentially depends on where you live and what the problem is. Here is a review of some major areas of concern:

Problems related to sexuality—The Family Planning Association provides clinical services throughout the country, as well as education and information programmes on human sexuality for schools, community groups and the general public. Some medical units will provide a greater range of contraceptive and other sexually related services as part of a broader service, as do women's health centres. Specific problems are also catered for in a variety of facilities.

- Where abortion is legal, a termination of pregnancy can be acquired through hospitals or special clinics (which vary in the quality of their supportive counselling and follow up)
- Sexually transmitted diseases are dealt with at hospitals or STD clinics (again with varying degrees of sensitivity)
- Support groups catering to the particular needs of gay adolescents are available in most towns and cities
- Rape Crisis Centres take a compassionate and broadbased approach; but there is practically nothing available to help offenders

School and education difficulties—Many problems can be sorted out within the education system, although there are needs which come within the province of health and welfare agencies:

- Some paediatric units and hospitals have a learning disabilities clinic
- Where underachievement has an emotional cause, or a child or teenager refuses to go to school, some sort of psychological intervention is needed (there are often psychologists, social workers or psychiatrists attached to community health centres)
- At present, neither education nor welfare departments are taking responsibility for teenagers who are truanting (going somewhere other than school), although some schools take it very seriously indeed

Career and employment—School career advisors and teachers will offer guidance in career choices (some schools go to a lot of trouble to help with these decisions, in fact), unemployed people of all ages become rather tied in to the Job Centre and quickly become familiar with its workings and limitations. Government-run Youth Opportunities Schemes and Youth Training Schemes offer unemployed young people not in full time education, an opportunity to be more able to support themselves while developing closer links with their community. The projects aim to improve the employability of their participants.

Nutrition and weight problems (including eating disorders)—There are nutritionists aplenty, eager to be consulted, and a plethora of dieting establishments. Few of the latter are particularly suited to teenagers (although Weight Watchers claim success with motivated young people). Young people with confirmed anorexia or bulimia need to be in the hands of professionals with experience in managing these difficult problems. In the first instance, these might be located at a special clinic or hospital; for the more seriously afflicted, admission to hospital (ideally in a specialised eating disorders unit) is indicated.

Athletics and sports medicine—As soon as possible after a sports injury occurs, it is important to get expert advice, preferably from someone who knows what they're doing (an increasing number of doctors are becoming interested in 'sports medicine', so it should be possible to find one). Sports medicine clinics in major cities (generally private) provide advice about sporting choices, training needs, orthopaedic and physiotherapy treatment, and may be able to tell you where to find skilled professionals in your area.

Chronic and disabling conditions—Chronically ill and disabled teenagers have access to a wide variety of health and related services, both government and voluntary. Specific organisations, many with employed staff, provide treatment, care, assistance, support and accommodation for a range of physical and mental handicaps, for example, diabetes, cystic fibrosis, thalasaemia and cancer.

Emotional/behavioural problems—Public mental health services in all states provide special services for adolescents through hospitals and community health centres, but not all problems are adequately catered for. In most instances, a community based psychosocial service having the capacity to provide a range of individual, group and family approaches is ideal, but these do not exist everywhere. There are also skilled professionals (psychologists, social workers and psychiatrists, for example) working in the private sector.

A gap in services is particularly notable for the following groups:

- Significantly acting out anti-social teenagers—breaking the law involves the police and the courts, and once in that system, it's notoriously hard to break out; 'basically good' kids who get incarcerated with hardened delinquents and adult criminals, don't stay basically good; what they need is intense input in structured environments, something our society has yet to provide
- Teenagers with drug and alcohol problems—ironically, despite community concern about this group (and the fact that it is as much a societal as a personal problem), there are relatively few youth facilities; of the adult services, only some offer youth components; Alateen, part of Alanon, is designed specifically to help the teenager with alcoholic parents
- Psychotic adolescents—have nowhere appropriate to go; there are no psychiatric holding wards specifically for very disturbed young people, so those requiring hospital treatment are housed with very disturbed adults
- Mildly retarded teenagers—also poorly catered for in the main
- Homeless young people—crisis accommodation is always in short supply; teenagers tend to become addicted to the youth refuge scene and often experience a downhill spiral (only the strongest make it)

Marital and family difficulties—Family therapy services are in reasonable supply (mostly through community health centres), but are poorly co-ordinated. For adults, Marriage Guidance Council centres are available almost everywhere, but don't cater for adolescents. Alternatively, teenagers from troubled homes can often find individual counsellors, when it is actually the family that needs to be taken on, so there may at times be the confusion of two separate agencies being involved.

Where to Get Information

There are a number of non-government organisations that can provide useful information concerning resources and services relevant to young people, parents and families.

Family Advice and Support

National Co-ordinating Committee of Self Help Groups
Mrs Jane Moss
10 Pakenham Road
Edgbaston
Birmingham

For parents under stress

National Stepfamily Association
Maris House
Maris Lane
Trumpington
Cambridgeshire
0223 841306

Health

Health Education Council
78 New Oxford Street
London WC1
01-637 1881

National Association for the Welfare of Children in Hospital
Exton House
Exton Street
London SE1
01-261 1738

Gives advice and campaigns for better conditions for children in hospital

Helplines

Capital Helpline
01-388 7575

Family Phone-in
01-341 1558

Can help with family problems

Message Home
01-799 7662

Twenty-four hour runaway to parent contact service

Samaritans
01-283 3400

Twenty-four hour listening ear if you are in despair

Youthline
0702 40804

Twenty-four hour service for discussing your problems

Single Parents

Families Need Fathers
37 Carden Road
London SE15
01-639 5362

Gingerbread
35 Wellington Street
London WC2
01-240 0953

Self-help association for single parents

National Council for One-Parent Families
255 Kentish Town Road
London NW5
01-267 1361

Offers support and advice

Counselling for Teenagers

Just Ask
11 Great Russell Street
London WC1
01-637 1333, extension 225

London Youth Advisory
26 Prince of Wales Road
London NW5
01-267 4792
and
31 Nottingham Place
London W1
01-935 8870 or 1219

Teenage Info Network
102 Harper Road
London SE1
01-403 2444

Under 21
398 Hoe Street
London E17
01-558 0811

Youth Aid
17 Brownhill Road
London SE6
01-697 2152

Advice on Drugs

Families Anonymous
88 Caledonian Road
London N7
01-278 8805

Will put you in touch with self-help drug abuse groups for families

Institute for the Study of Drugs Dependence (ISDD)
1-4 Hatton Place
London EC1

Library and information service only

SCODA (Standing Conference on Drug Abuse)
1-4 Hatton Place
London EC1
01-430 2341

Full list of drug counselling agencies throughout the country

Youth Organisations

Association for Jewish Youth
AJY House
Lindley Street
London E1
01-790 6407

Central London Youth Project
29 Shelton Street
London WC2
01-240 3266

Muslim Youth Association
31 Draycott Place
London SW3
01-584 6364

Bibliography

Anderson, J. *Teen is a Four Letter Word: A Survival Guide for Parents*. Betterway Publications, Virginia, 1983

Bennett, D. *Adolescent Health in Australia—An Overview of Needs and Approaches to Care*. A health education and promotion monograph. The Australian Medical Association, Sydney, International Youth Year 1985

Bennett, D. (ed.) *Problems of Adolescents at Work and at Play*. Australian Association for Adolescent Health, Sydney, 1985

Berman, E. *The New Fashioned Parent—How to Make Your Family Style Work*. Prentice Hall, Inc, Englewood Cliffs, New Jersey, 1980

Bloomfield, H. with Felder, L. *Making Peace with Your Parents: The Key to Enriching Your Life and All Your Relationships*. Ballantine Books, New York, 1983

The Boston Women's Health Book Collective. *Ourselves and Our Children—A Book By and For Parents*. Random House, New York, 1978

Collins, J. K. and Harper, J. F. *The Adolescent Boy—An Australian Analysis*. Cassell Australia, 1978

Collins, J. K. and Harper, J. F. *The Adolescent Girl—An Australian Analysis*. Cassell Australia, 1978

Conger, J. *Adolescence–Generation Under Pressure*. A Life Cycle Book, Nelson, Melbourne, 1979

Daniel, W. Jnr. *Adolescents in Health and Disease*. The C. V. Mosby Company, Saint Louis, 1977

Davitz, L. & J. *How to Live (Almost) Happily With a Teenager*. Dove Communications, Melbourne, 1982

Dowse, S. *Leaving School, It's Harder for Girls*. Y.W.C.A., Sydney, 1983

Ellard, J. *Middle Age*, Modern Medicine of Australia, August, 1983

Ginott, H. G. *Between Parent & Teenager*. Avon Books, New York, 1969

Group for the Advancement of Psychiatry. *The Joys and Sorrows of Parenthood*. Report No 84, 1973

Hartin, W. W. *Divorce Dilemma—A Guide to Divorcing People*. Hill of Content, Melbourne, 1977

Johnson, S. *The One Minute Mother*. Columbus Books, London, 1984

Katchadourian, H. *The Biology of Adolescence*. W. H. Freeman and Company, San Francisco, 1977

Konopka, G. *Young girls—A Portrait of Adolescence*. Prentice-Hall, Inc, Englewood Cliffs, New Jersey, 1976

Lake, T. *Relationships—The Complete Guide to Understanding Yourself and Other People*. Michael Joseph, London, 1981

Lawton, A. *Parents and Teenagers*. Unwin Paperbacks, London, 1985

Leach, K. *What Everyone Should Know About Drugs*. Sheldon Press, London, 1983

McCarthy, W. & Gordon, S. *Raising Your Child Responsibly in a Sexually Permissive Society*. Collins, Sydney, 1984

Neinstein, L. *Adolescent Health Care*. Urban & Schwarzburg, Baltimore, Munich, 1984

Raporport, R. & R. & Strelitz, Z. *Fathers, Mothers and Others—Towards New Alliances*. University of Queensland Press, Brisbane, 1977

Rogers, D. *The Adult Years—An Introduction to Aging*. Prentice Hall, Inc, Englewood Cliffs, New Jersey, 1975

Schowalter, J. E. & Anyan, W. R. *The Family Handbook of Adolescence*. Alfred A. Knopf, New York, 1981

Wilson, J. *The Teenager and You*. Hedges and Bell Pty Ltd, Melbourne, 1982

Index